When the Heartbeat Stops

Organic Accounts of Women Breaking the Silence Around Miscarriage

JaRonda Dockett

DEDICATION

For Faith, Justin, and all the loved babies gone too soon.

For Andrea, Jen, Aleix, Lucy, Taylor, and all the women navigating life after miscarriage.

CONTENTS

ACKNOWLEDGMENTS

Through every trial and triumph in my life, You have been a constant. Holy Spirit, this book would've been another idea come and gone were it not for an extra nudge from you. Jesus, I'm beyond grateful.

To my husband Vince, there aren't adequate words to properly thank you for your love, support, and understanding through everything marriage has thrown at us these past two years. Thank you for your listening ear, comforting embrace, and encouraging prayers.

To my parents. I am so blessed to be your daughter. Mommy, thank you for being my first editing eye and for always supporting me to follow all of my dreams. Daddy, I'm pretty sure my writing swag comes from you. You've already lovingly declared the book a bestseller and who am I to disagree?

To my sisters Kia and Nickki. Thank you for being a shoulder to cry on and offering to do whatever I needed. Y'all are gonna be the best aunties!

To my Bride Tribe: Annena, Angel, and Shana. There are not adequate words to say thanks for decades of friendship, love, and support. Thanks for riding the rollercoaster with me and joining in to feel all the feels that came along with both miscarriages.

To Maki and Richie. Your love and support of Vince and I has been nothing short of amazing. I am truly blessed to call you friends.

To Rich and Celeste. Your love and care for Vince and I could always be felt, even from three states away. We can always count on y'all to keep it 100.

To Brie. Your friendship has been a priceless gem. Your empathetic conversations validated me on so many days. Your vibranium treats kept us going. Vince and I are so appreciative.

To Lauren and Mikhal. Thank you for setting your eyes on the toughest of rough drafts and giving me your candid initial feedback. Your encouragement and prayers throughout this process have been much appreciated.

To Ms. Jewell. The words "You can write a book, Doc" that you said in a phone conversation with me were confirmation of a fleece prayer I made. Thanks for letting the Lord use you!

To my Stanton fam. Y'all are amazing individuals. Your commitment to seeing Black excellence reign in our kiddos is unwavering. That remains the goal despite the barrage of obstacles each day. Y'all have been with me through the highs of Vince's proposal to the lows of our pregnancy losses. I'm grateful to count you all as family.

To my family. I've been so blessed to have a village of aunties, uncles, cousins, and in-laws who have always been in my corner and pushed me to be my best. Thank y'all for being you.

To my friends near and far, from MAHS to Means Hall to the Tree and CYDC, thanks for your friendship for whatever period of time. Our paths crossed along this journey and you hold a special place in my heart.

To Seeking His Face Small Group and my church families at Grace and Mercy, FBCG, and Zion. Thank you for your comfort, prayers, and encouragement.

To Brian Keith Harris II. Thank you for taking the time on your morning walk to talk to me about self-publishing. I'm looking forward to your next book!

To Ms. Lydia. Thank you for allowing me to use the engagement photo you took for the back cover. Your photos are as amazingly brilliant as you are.

To my cover artist Jennifer Wang. You truly brought our conversation to life. I could not have pictured a more beautiful, more perfect visual to represent this work. Thank you for sharing your talent with me!

To my editor Lynelle Herndon - Thank you for working day and night through virtual learning schedules to meet our deadlines. Your thoughtful and straightforward feedback continually pushed me to provide more imagery, more clarity and more connection for the reader. You've helped make this work truly exceptional.

To Kyle Dendy. You made me believe I could do this work. I did not think I would leave a Youth Day sermon at my grandfather's church inspired to publish a book. Your guidance given through Book Launch On Demand led me from a draft to a published product. I wouldn't be a published author if it weren't for you.

To Jen, Andrea, Aleix, Lucy, and Taylor. There would be no book without your willingness to share your miscarriage story with me. Your vulnerability and candor helped to create a product that is raw and relatable. You are amazing women and I love you all dearly.

To you, the reader. Thank you for your purchase! I don't take it for granted that you chose to spend your hard-earned coins on this book. If you are a woman who has experienced a pregnancy loss, I hope you saw yourself somewhere in this book. I pray this book frees you and those around you from the strongholds of awkward silences. I hope it sparks you to talk about miscarriage openly and explore the reasons why these lost babies become hushed secrets.

1 JARONDA'S STORY

"First comes love, then comes marriage, then comes the baby in the baby carriage." I, like many young girls, grew up singing this tune with no real connection to what the words meant. I just understood that this was supposed to be the proper order of things. And like the good Christian girl that I was always labeled to be, I did my best to follow said order. What the nursery rhyme didn't tell me was how long it would take to find love… or find a love that is also committed to marriage… or find a love that is also committed to marriage and creating a family… or how long it would be before me and that man actually brought life into this world.

On March 23, 2014 I began dating the person that would become "that man" – my husband Vince. Four years later we married and started getting busy! I mean, we had waited four years to have intercourse, so needless to say, the fire was burning, and we were both excited to consummate our marriage. We were also both ready for children, and while we wanted them soon, neither one of us felt pressed to put ourselves on a timeline. We agreed to have sex without any birth control and see what the Lord had planned for us.

Within two months we were pregnant! We were both shocked at how quickly it happened. I had known a couple of friends and family members who struggled with infertility and had a small glimpse into their pain. I didn't know what the road would look like for Vince and I, and I was relieved to see that apparently my eggs and his sperm were doing great.

At least I thought everything was great. I remember how difficult it was to be genuinely happy when the doctor told me I was pregnant because the cramping had me in so much pain at the time. I had been one of those lucky ladies who enjoyed relatively mild periods all through my early 20s. When I did have cramps, they tended to happen just on the first couple days of my cycle. On those days, my best friend Advil and I would link up and then everything was fine. But these were a different kind of cramp, nothing like anything I'd experienced before. This was a stay-curled-up-in-the-fetal-position-because-something-is-punching-my-uterus-and-poking-me-in-my-vagina-simultaneously kind of cramp.

I was only a few days late for my cycle and the thought that I could be pregnant did cross my mind, but I wanted to wait a little while longer before taking a test and getting my hopes crushed. I was also worried about a positive result because I had never been pregnant before, but I didn't think that severe cramping was normal. Already it seemed like something was wrong. My husband tried everything to help me with the pain, all the while secretly hoping the pain was a small side effect of a baby blessing. He drove me to urgent care to get things checked out and I received two diagnoses: I had bacterial vaginosis, and I was pregnant.

I don't recall much about leaving urgent care that September night, other than a really giddy Vince driving us home. My mind was swarming with questions. *How quickly will this antibiotic stop the cramping pain? Is the baby going to have sickle cell disease like me? Where will we put a baby in our one-bedroom apartment? Oh my gosh, didn't I just drink a margarita yesterday? Who will be the delivery doctor? When should we start telling folks? How does my maternity time work if I deliver after the school year is over? Who just had a baby that we can borrow stuff from?* The list went on and on. It was somewhat humorous that the nature of the questions largely didn't match up with how far along I was. My body was only four weeks into a 40 week-long journey, but my mind started pelting questions at me as if my bundle of joy was coming tomorrow.

Almost immediately I began an Internet search to find whatever I could about diet and exercise during pregnancy. These were both areas I struggled with before pregnancy, so I couldn't imagine how I would be able to get a handle on changing these habits almost instantaneously. Consistency with self-care routines had never been my strong suit. I knew that my habitual lack of discipline in those areas would not just have repercussions for me, but also for my unborn child. It was a daunting thing to contemplate how my weaknesses would be magnified in my seed. I was already feeling like a failure in motherhood and I'd only been pregnant one day!

The next six weeks were kind of a blur. Each follow-up visit to the doctor seemed to hold a new surprise or development. First, I discovered that I had lost weight, which was actually due to the fact that I was being very intentional about increasing my vegetable and fruit intake. Then I got my first ultrasound, and when I showed Vince the picture, he couldn't contain his excitement. Though we hadn't discussed when we would tell people, he just couldn't wait any longer. He'd fallen in love when he saw the photo of his child and he wanted the world to know. But I convinced him that we should start with just our parents. While waiting for my turn at the lab to schedule my glucose test and have my blood drawn for genetic testing, he quickly snapped some pics and texted both our families the good news.

Vince and our parents and siblings were brimming with excitement, but for some reason I found it difficult to be genuinely thrilled. All I kept doing was praying. I completed a weekly journal that had Bible scriptures related to whatever part of the body was being formed in the baby that week. Meanwhile my hubby would be kissing my belly and talking to Fay-Fay. Though we had no idea what the sex of the baby would be, we somehow felt it was a girl and named her Faith, or Fay-Fay for short. We also told a few co-workers about our expected bundle of joy but decided to wait until after the first trimester to make anything public. Even in sharing the news with my close friends at work, their excitement was always much greater than mine. It's like I somehow knew that Fay-Fay wouldn't be with me for long.

Vince's best friend Rich had invited us up to New York for a concert over Veteran's Day weekend. They hadn't seen each other since our wedding in July so I automatically knew that we would go. We rented a car, packed it up for the short, four-hour trip from Maryland, and were on our way. I'm not sure if it was the type of car we rented or the pavement of the New York roads, but I felt every bump, lump and pothole almost the entire ride. The pain was less severe than the cramps I had from bacterial vaginosis, but it hung around for longer. The whole trip would be filled with abdominal discomfort – a figurative thorn in my side.

Vince could tell I was uncomfortable during the car ride, and he stopped often so I could stretch, pee and walk around. When we finally made it to New York, I think we were in Rich's apartment for all of five minutes before my better half whipped out the sonogram. I didn't even know he'd brought it with him. Rich and his girlfriend Celeste were ecstatic for us. Even their 10-month-old daughter looked happy when Vince shared the news. And this was another joyous moment where I felt lukewarm compared to everyone else in the room.

The New York trip had a lot of fun highlights. I met up with my college roommate and ate at a delicious barbecue joint. As she sat across from us with her husband and son, she asked us about starting a family. Vince and I just replied that we were working on it, trying hard to not spill the beans about our bun in the oven.

With Rich and Celeste, we ate pizza and played board games one night. I won many, many times and earned the nickname Queen of Games. We went to an arcade with a bowling alley. Celeste commented that she wasn't sure if pregnant women were allowed to bowl. That was something I had never thought about, so of course I took to the Internet immediately. There were a couple posts that suggested abstaining from the activity, but overwhelmingly the websites stated that bowling was permissible. And since I love bowling, and winning, I couldn't resist.

The New York trip also had many lowlights. In addition to the bumpy car ride and the lingering pain, I couldn't sleep at night. The bed was way too soft, and the couch mattress was too springy. On top of that, I had to keep waking up in the middle of the night to use the bathroom. I was exhausted. The last thing an exhausted pregnant lady wants to do is go to a concert. But since it was a concert for a jazz musician, I figured it would be a chill affair where I could sit and relax most of the time.

Imagine my surprise to arrive at the concert and see crowds of people standing around. I spotted a small roped-off area with folding chairs that was a little more elevated than the general standing area. I wondered if you had to pay to sit there and how quickly I could become a VIP. Turns out it was cool to sit there if you were an expectant mother, but not if you were friends of an expectant mother. Vince and I headed to the folding chairs while Rich and Celeste migrated to the standing section. We would each be able to enjoy the concert, but not together. And not for long. Those folding chairs were so uncomfortable that I only made it an hour into the concert before I let Vince know it was time to go.

The first night back at home I was grateful to be in my bed, but I still couldn't sleep. I called and made a doctor appointment for first thing the next morning. When I went to the doctor, she told me that some cramping is normal and that each pregnancy is different. She said my cervix was closed and that was a great thing, a sign that the baby was doing good. An open cervix would have told her a miscarriage was happening. While her words were a sign of relief to me, I remained perplexed. Something just felt off to me, but I kept hearing that things looked fine.

The doctor also told me the results of my glucose test. I was diagnosed with gestational diabetes. I cried and I cried and I cried. I have multiple family members who have been diagnosed as diabetic and pre-diabetic. Several years ago, I was even considered pre-diabetic and had to prick my finger daily to check my blood sugar levels. Seeing the vision and mobility consequences my diagnosed family members were juggling, I had done everything I could to lower my sugar and stay off the diabetes radar. This gestational diabetes news devastated me. My mind was swept into a black hole of potential consequences - pregnancy complications, daily medication, vision degeneration - that might occur with this diagnosis.

After about 15 minutes, I was calm enough to listen to the nurse explain to me the steps I needed to take. While I listened to the nurse talk about food logs, pricking my finger and glucose trackers, I couldn't get the image of my uncle lying in bed after his foot amputation out of my head. I fought back the tears and then rushed to the parking garage, a huge bag of needles, alcohol pads and food trackers in tow. The nurse said repeatedly that having gestational diabetes doesn't mean diabetes will remain after pregnancy. But I knew that there was a greater chance for me to develop type 2 diabetes due to my family history, and I couldn't shake the feeling that things had gone from bad to worse.

I would love to say that the next day, November 15, 2018, started off like any other day. But nothing could be further from the truth. I looked at the unexpected snowflakes outside my window and got ready for work thinking *This is gonna be a crazy day!* There was a snow squall of sorts outside, but the meteorologist had not included heavy snowfall in the day's forecast. I knew I was going to have low class attendance, so I was actually excited to go to work. I ended up only having eight students come that day. I started teaching per usual, beginning with our phonics program in a circle on the carpet. Seeing that no other students had arrived by that time, I pretty much declared that day "a wash" in my head and let the students choose literacy center activities that they could do independently.

Probably about 30 minutes into their free play, I noticed that I had abdominal pain that steadily increased. I remember being curled up in the fetal position in the library section of my classroom. The fact that I was laying on the floor in the classroom, head on a germ-ladened pillow from the children's library, was another strong indicator for me that something was seriously wrong. One of my colleagues, Ms. Richardson, came into the room and noticed me on the floor. Seeing this anomaly, she urged me to go home and said she would take my class for the afternoon.

So I left work early, around 11:30 a.m., and in the parking lot I saw one of my parents coming to pick her son up early. The snow had stopped by now, but still covered the streets and sidewalks around most parts of the neighborhood. I ended up telling her that I was pregnant, not feeling well and leaving early for the day.

After the mom's quick congratulations, she launched into story after story about pregnancy complications and incompatible cervixes. And in my mind, I'm like *Lady, these are NOT the stories people want to hear when they are in their first pregnancy and not feeling well.* I barely listened as I grasped for an exit line, scurrying into the car as politely and swiftly as possible.

I headed to the rental car company to return the car. The whole car ride I sat on a library pillow I had taken from my classroom, hoping it would ameliorate the pain. While the pillow made the trip slightly more comfortable, the pain did not subside. I arrived at the rental car return relieved that I was one step closer to home. I needed to call a rideshare company to come and pick me up, so I waited in the lounge of the car dealership for a couple minutes. Thinking it smart to use the restroom before leaving, I quickly headed to pee before my ride arrived.

As soon as I exited the one-stall bathroom, teacher bag and pillow in hand, I found that I needed to go back in. Out of nowhere it felt like I peed myself after I had just peed! I looked down and saw little brown spots on the pristine dealership floor. I immediately started saying aloud, "No, no, no." An older gentleman, possibly an employee, came up to me and asked if everything was okay. I frantically replied, "No, I think I might be losing my baby." and vanished into the men's restroom (because of course someone was using the one-stall women's restroom at that time).

I plopped down on the toilet and felt a whoosh come out. And as I was sitting on the toilet, my child's life pouring out of me into a bowl of no return, my phone rang. The driver had arrived and was looking for me. Fighting back tears, I answered and let him know, "I'm coming. I'm coming." As I stood up from the toilet, I looked down into the abyss of red and brown. But floating in the middle of it all I saw something else – a white, wispy, cotton-ball-esque object. Though I only glanced, I just knew it was her. I knew. And I had only seconds to process it all before I had to flush.

I still had the pillow that I was using for comfort in the rental car, and I was glad I had it for this car ride now. I had no idea what was going to happen next. *Would I bleed in the car? Was anything else gonna come out of me? Would the pillow absorb everything? Would I have to pay a cleaning fee for having a miscarriage in the car?* As all this was running through my mind, I was telling my driver to take me to urgent care instead of my home. The driver repeatedly stated back that I needed to change it in the app. In my frazzled state, I was on my phone pushing all types of buttons, trying to figure out how to change my destination since I very rarely used ride shares.

Then I had to make the dreadful call to my husband. I can imagine him sitting in full security uniform at the front desk, frozen in a state of shock when I told him, "I think I lost the baby." Of course, he quickly replied that he would meet me at urgent care. I also call my friend Makeda who teaches with me. She has a beautiful spirit and a true heart for chasing after the things of Christ and I knew her presence would be a blessing. On top of that, she and her husband lived seven minutes down the road from our apartment.

Amidst all the uncertainty and pain, somehow the rational side of me was already thinking *How are we going to get home?* I had just returned the rental car and Vince didn't drive to work that day. Before I'd even arrived, I was thinking how awful it would be to leave urgent care and take the bus or train or even taxi home after experiencing this most painful loss.

The whole car ride I kept praying, "Lord, please save my baby." I knew Faith was already gone but praying was the only thing I knew to do. If ever there were a time for the Lord to work a miracle, this would be it. I desperately clung to any minute possibility of a miracle. My faith dangled on the last sliver of hope that was left. The ride to urgent care felt like an eternity, but at the same time, I didn't want it to end. It was almost like getting out of the car made it official, because I knew that someone in that building was going to tell me that Faith was gone.

I was whisked back into a room, and Vince rushed in five minutes after I arrived. Vince helped me change into my hospital gown and helped me to the exam room table. As I was approaching the exam table, another whoosh happened. I was screaming, "Something else came out of me!" The nurses and doctors rushed over to collect the blood and tissue samples, murmuring about what each part might be. I felt sticky and messy all down my thighs, and at that point, I just wanted it all to be over.

Squeezing my hubby's hand, I stared at the ceiling and let my eyes fall shut for a moment. I wriggled my way to the top of the exam table and "assumed the position" for a vaginal ultrasound. The cold, intrusive feeling of the exam was physically and emotionally magnified since the purpose of the poking and prodding was to confirm the absence of a fetus. As the technician continued to find the right angles and take pictures, she started asking me questions about my fibroids. I looked at her in disbelief and let out an exasperated sigh before retorting, "What are you talking about? No one has ever told me I have fibroids before!"

"Oh yeah," she says. "I can feel three of them right here."

Seriously?!?! Something else is wrong with my uterus? How could we possibly, at that moment, be adding fuel to this fire? So she finished up the exam and I pretty much laid there in shock, continuing to hold Vince's hand. Outside of the fibroids, the technician didn't make any other comments. She continued to adjust the camera and snap some pictures on the computer. When the exam was over, she guided us to a room to await the official results from the doctor.

I don't know of a metaphor that could encapsulate the anticipation, hope, agony, fear and worry that simultaneously filled those moments of waiting. Moments later the doctor entered and said, "Mrs. Dockett, sorry to confirm that you did have a miscarriage." After he exits, Vince and I just hold each other and all I could do was cry. Just cry. We didn't have any words. There just were no words. Our precious gift was gone so suddenly.

Vince stepped outside when Makeda arrived, and she didn't have any words either. I remember crying into her shoulder and her whispering to me, "I can keep holding you. I can hold you tighter." And the tears kept flowing. At the time Makeda was also pregnant and our due dates were only three weeks apart from each other. We were so excited to experience our first pregnancy together and had already etched play dates onto our future calendars. In my mind I couldn't fathom why all of this was happening. At the appointment yesterday the doctor said everything was fine. The cervix was closed. This wasn't supposed to happen.

Then a nurse handed me a sanitary napkin, interrupting my thoughts. Honestly, the logistics after the experience just seemed so heartless and routine. I was bleeding out while my miscarriage finished running its course. And then she hands me one stupid, cheap hospital pad with no wings and flimsy coverings. Shouldn't medical centers have the best pads? And then on top of that, I had to put back on the soaked, bloodstained, mucus-saturated pants that I wore into the urgent care. In that moment it was like reliving the miscarriage all over again, one pant leg at a time.

We head to Makeda's car to take the long ride home. It wasn't an awkward ride per se, but it was relatively quiet, both knowing we were going home to a different life than we had planned. Makeda, being so thoughtful, stopped at the local drugstore and brought me some real pads, ibuprofen and some ice cream.

When I think back to arriving home that evening, I can't remember what the first moments were like or even what it was like getting ready for bed. I do remember three specific things that I did. First, I threw my gray pants and purple underwear away almost immediately. Though purple is my favorite color, I haven't worn purple underwear since. Second, I put on the pads from the store and some comfy pajamas. Third, I took my final trip to the bathroom for the day.

I pulled down my underwear and there atop of my fresh pad was a huge, palm-sized red glob. Just sitting there. So big in fact, it looked like it should've fallen off to the side and down my pajama pant leg before I made it to the bathroom. Picking it up, I was surprised at its texture. It wasn't sticky or runny like I expected. It was smooth and whole. I pushed it with my fingertips, and it was squishy, bouncing back without indentation.

I took some moments to stare at it, wondering what this was supposed to be for my baby. Was this the placenta, the part that was supposed to give her life inside of me? I sat and held it in my hand, and I couldn't stop thinking that this was supposed to give her life and now it was all taken away. And now it seemed things had come full circle – me and her and the toilet again. But this time I had time to say goodbye.

"When a child loses his parent, they are called an orphan. When a spouse loses her or his partner, they are called a widow or widower. When parents lose their child, there isn't a word to describe them." President Ronald Reagan's words hit the nail on the head. Indescribable. There are no words to accurately articulate the level of sorrow, anguish, helplessness, anger, and at times shame and guilt, that come with the death of a child. Losing Faith was not the first traumatic event that's happened in my life, but it was the first time that I ever felt lingering grief; the grief that follows you around like the one dark rainy cloud in a sky of sun rays. It's a weightiness you can't get out from under, a sadness that you have no more tears for, and an emptiness of sinkhole proportions.

Dealing with grief isn't typically a subject taught in school or a topic for dinner conversations, so like most folks, I wasn't exactly sure how to move forward after the miscarriage. As a teacher I've had a few trainings on understanding trauma and grief in order to recognize signs in my students and families. It's hard to remember all the details, but I held onto the big rocks. Grief never goes away. Every individual grieves differently and on a unique timeline. The extent that the person feels weighed down by grief changes over time, depending on the presence or absence of certain triggers. I tried to keep all of this in mind as I began to let the reality of what had happened sink into my mind, body, and spirit. *I am no longer pregnant. Fay-Fay isn't here. We aren't having a baby.*

Remembering the sequence of events after arriving home is difficult, as it all seems like a big blur of sadness. I spent the next couple days crying into Vince's shoulder more times than I can count. We lay cuddled in bed, with little appetite or desire for movement. We didn't even need to speak. We just held each other.

By the third day I realized I hadn't seen Vince cry yet. This was very concerning to me as I knew how excited he was about our child and I knew he was just as heartbroken as I was. I talked with him about it and he admitted he was trying to be strong for me. I thanked him for that, but also let him know that I needed him to be sad *with* me, instead of trying to be strong *for* me. We both took time to journal and write down our thoughts as a way to process, and eventually we did cry together. Gospel music blared through the home to ease the silence and cover the wails of our heartache. I can vividly remember a day where Vince was in his man-cave with the same song on repeat, while I was in the bedroom lying prostrate on the floor screaming Jesus's name repeatedly.

Then the time came when our grief could no longer remain private. People who had only known for days that we were pregnant were now receiving texts that we were not. Decisions had to be made if we would communicate the miscarriage to close family and friends who we hadn't told about the pregnancy yet. I felt every text was etching Faith's name onto a tombstone. She really wasn't coming back.

Outwardly I was a mess and internally I wasn't doing much better. My silent conversations were glaringly dichotomous. One train of thought was filled with questions. *Did I exercise too little? Was it the romaine I ate? Did I sleep on my right side on the couch? Did I spend too much time in the car? Should I have sat out of bowling? Should I have questioned the doctor more about my cramping? Was it my glucose level? Did I speak positively over her enough? Did I have an attitude of joy? Did I complain too much? Did I pray too little? Was I on my feet too much? Did I have enough iron?*

It felt as if everyone, including my OB/GYN who thoughtfully called me a couple days later, said there was nothing I could've done to cause this miscarriage. *But it happened much later than most,* I would say to myself. I felt it had to be something I did because we were so close to the 13-week mark, the so-called "safe zone" (in quotes because that zone doesn't exist!). My train of thought continued to navigate its way down the logic track, as I was determined to find a "why" behind the miscarriage. But alas, I was not in control.

Surprisingly, the other train of thought that flooded my mind was filled with gratitude. This, I think, may be a best-kept secret to managing grief. The timing of everything happened in a way that I could look back and see God's care in the midst of the storm. Ms. Richardson volunteered to take my class. I left school in time to return the rental car back without having a miscarriage in the car. I was near a restroom when the water and blood began dripping down my legs. I was driven to urgent care ASAP, and I didn't bleed in that car either. My husband arrived at urgent care almost immediately after I did. The miscarriage happened naturally. Makeda was able to give us a ride home. Oddly enough, I could easily find "silver linings" galore amidst that storm, and each one filled me with overwhelming gratitude.

Then my village swooped in, and it was like an outward signal to stay focused on gratitude. Vince's family came over to spend a day with us. My parents drove down from Pennsylvania to stay with us for the weekend. Friends from work came over with food, desserts and handmade "We miss you!" cards from students. Prayer texts were sent that reminded me to circle promises of scripture like Jeremiah 29:11 (NIV), "'For I know the plans I have for you,' declares the Lord, 'plans to prosper you and not to harm you, plans to give you hope and a future.'" And Romans 8:28 (NIV), "And we know that in all things God works for the good of those who love him, who have been called according to his purpose." Flowers and cards arrived at our door. The outpouring of love and comfort from those closest to us was amazing. Weeks and months later, our village still checked in on us. I am forever grateful for their steadfast presence in our lives.

I am also grateful for my husband's courage and initiative to do the one thing I wasn't sure I could do – sign us up for counseling. We went to a counseling session with the pastor who married us. With this tragic event happening in the infancy of our marriage, we were grateful that this loss seemed to be bringing us closer together rather than tearing us apart. Our pastor urged us to have set times for our outward expressions of grief – crying, yelling, screaming – which happened daily at first. We also talked about how losing Faith would change our perspectives moving forwards, and what our dreams and fears might look like in those weeks immediately following the miscarriage. He left us meditating on a biblical response to a boy born blind in John 9:3 (NIV), "'Neither this man nor his parents sinned,' said Jesus, 'but this happened so that the works of God might be displayed in him.'"

Emerging from your home after losing a child is like walking on eggshells. Cracklings happen with each step as you are bombarded with babies. Never before did you realize how babies are everywhere! They're at schools, on social media feeds, on buses, on commercials, in churches, in sermons, in movies. Sometimes right besides those babies is a mommy, or maybe a pregnant mommy. Since the world is populated with babies and mommies, the triggers to remind you of the most horrible day of your life are inescapable.

Because of this, I think losing a child is a unique trauma. It is one where you cannot minimize or control what might trigger intense emotions connected to your grief. I experienced this flood of emotion my first day back at work. Holding back tears, I walked into the office and straight to the sign-in book. As I was prepared to do the same to make it to my classroom for a good private cry, my principal waved me into her office. I flopped down in the chair and began to bawl. I couldn't comprehend how I was going to be able to look at my class full of babies – babies that made it into this world – and continue teaching so matter-of-factly.

My principal let me know that I didn't have to that today. As a woman who had been through two miscarriages herself before having a daughter, she was extremely empathetic to my mixed bag of emotions and I was relieved to not have to put on a façade for her. After a little more conversation, I realized that I didn't want to go home and sulk. It was time to be back at work and I would get through this day like I did all the others. The strength of the Lord and the support of my village would give me enough grace for the day.

I would need a double helping of grace to embrace another difficult post-miscarriage experience – baby showers. As the Lord would have it, I'm in a profession dominated by women, and so each year the chances of multiple colleagues having a baby are pretty high. Once you add friends and family into that equation, the number of new babies becomes exponential. In the month after my miscarriage I received three texts and saw one Facebook post of friends who were announcing they were expecting. These were supposed to be the folks I was pregnant with, the girls I could go to for play dates and mommy advice, the crew to be on maternity leave together. But now I was out of that crowd.

It's awkward being the childless mom at a baby shower. You have conversations and participate in the games to the extent you can, but the whole time you are thinking *This was supposed to be me*. Usually only me or maybe me and one other person in the room knows my story, so I'm sure I seem like every other baby shower attendee. But going to a baby shower after a miscarriage also gives you perspective. You realize that you also don't know anyone else's story in the room. That all the baby shower attendees have their own story, and though it may not have included miscarriage, it could've been just as painful. And it's why I will never casually ask someone, "So when y'all gonna have a baby?"

As soon as we were able, we wanted to try again. It's so interesting to write the words "try again" because we didn't try at all the first time, it just happened. We weren't using apps or measuring anything; we just had sex, that's it. Something that seemed so simple had skyrocketed to being super complex.

I had an MRI to pinpoint the locations and measure the sizes of the fibroids. I hoped I would be able to have a minimally invasive laparoscopic surgery for the fibroid removal. Unfortunately, at the consultation the doctor revealed that I did not have three, but more like 16 fibroids. Those three were just the largest and most visible with the ultrasound technology. With that number of fibroids, I would have to have a more invasive myomectomy. But the doctor also said we could choose to keep trying. He pointed to some areas that were still prime for the baby to implant and said that healthy pregnancies with fibroids were possible. Vince and I left the office feeling defeated about the surgery, yet still confident that the Lord would bless us with a child.

So that's where we remain still – confidently planted in a hopeful place. It's been nine months since we lost Faith, and we are about to enter a crossroad of decision. We're not sure what our next step will be. But I'm blessed to figure it all out with a husband who is loving, prayerful, supportive and just as eager as I to feel that first kick.

2 ANDREA'S STORY

I've always wanted to be a mom. So many of us know from the time we are wearing Sunday dresses and Mary Janes that being a mom is what we want to do. I lost my mother at a young age and I missed her beyond words when I was growing up. Even as a little girl I would think about how many kids I would have, what their names would be, what they might look like, what their personalities might be. But when I thought about being a mom someday, I didn't really think about the process of becoming a mom. It never crossed my mind that things wouldn't work out according to my plan.

When starting the journey to motherhood, having a miscarriage wasn't something I feared. Because women don't typically have a first appointment until eight weeks along, I began my first pregnancy thinking everything was going fine. Morning sickness, check. Breast tenderness, check. Slight weight gain in the waist, check. Getting up at night to pee, check. Everything was normal. All the signs of pregnancy were there. Until it was time to find a heartbeat. And there was none.

I was a shell of myself trying to process that news in the moment. My bundle of joy was gone, and my dream of motherhood was turning into a nightmare. I had to have a dilation and curettage, or D&C. I walked into it blindly, not really knowing much about the procedure. They go in and cut and vacuum out the womb. The process sounded like having an abortion to me. I was asleep the whole time, so I don't really know. I just remember

15

feeling empty afterward. I hemorrhaged a little and had a lot of cramping.

After having that D&C, I feared the doctors were wrong. Was a D&C necessary? Was it just too soon to hear the heartbeat? Those questions drove me insane, so I let my second miscarriage happen naturally. My body absorbed the baby in my third miscarriage. I never received an explanation as to why my body did that. In each miscarriage I would think I am carrying a child that is no longer alive and I'm just waiting for my body to reject this blessing. It was such an impossible thing to reconcile with myself.

Three miscarriages are normal. That's what the doctors told me. I was shocked to hear how common miscarriages were. About 20% of pregnancies end in miscarriage they said. Miscarriage is viewed scientifically as a process that happens to naturally rid the body of a fetus developing improperly. This perspective came through in the doctors' explanation, causing them to appear stoic and without compassion. While listening I couldn't help but think *Hey, I get it - miscarriage is common, but don't treat me and my baby like we're just another drop in the miscarriage statistic bucket.*

The worst part was the doctors didn't provide any explanation or information about why the miscarriage happened. No additional testing was done afterward to try and discover what might have happened. Because of the commonplace nature of miscarriages, standard procedures were observed, and no follow-up was done for my first three pregnancies. But maybe if the status quo wasn't strictly adhered to, my situation could have been different.

After the third miscarriage, doctors finally began to run tests. They found out that my body didn't produce enough progesterone, so I began to take supplements. My husband and I thought we knew what was going on. The doctors had diagnosed a problem and we were doing everything we were told to do in order to find a solution. But it hadn't worked.

I had a fourth miscarriage. My body never naturally expelled the fetus, and I had to have another D&C. Because the baby chose to stay around, I started to think *Does that mean that everything is okay? Should we do another ultrasound?* Again these questions drove me mad.

We tried for two years to conceive again after that fourth miscarriage. Conceiving was difficult because in addition to the low progesterone count, I didn't ovulate regularly. I had to take the fertility drug Clomid once a week in order to get pregnant. Every month our bathroom was littered with ovulation kits. Home pregnancy tests were stored under my sink. They became a bathroom staple, like toilet paper, that I could never be without. I would think to myself *I'm a day late*, I'd take the test and it would be negative. I told myself *It's too early; let me take another one in two days.* It was still negative. *Well, I didn't use my first morning pee. Let me do it again with my first morning pee.* I'd swear I saw a faint line. The bathroom trash can had become a graveyard for negative pregnancy tests.

Getting pregnant and staying pregnant was all I ever thought about. It consumed me. I was intentional about the food I ate, the exercises I did, how I slept, even what I read. There was a constant thought that there was something else I needed to do in order to make the pregnancy stick.

I know during this time my husband Fred was hurting, too. It was hard for him to support me while processing his own grief as well. He wanted to be a father just as bad as I wanted to be a mother. The pain after miscarriage is slightly different for the mother, though. As a mother you are connected to your baby right away. I wanted Fred to have that connection, too. I wanted him rubbing my belly and talking to the baby, but he didn't want to do that and grow a bond with a baby that might not exist. He wanted to wait until he held the baby in his arms to be connected.

At that moment I remember being so angry. There was no one to be angry at, so I would turn my rage and wrath toward my husband. I would say things like, "You're not as mad as me!" "You didn't take the time to get connected to them!" You just want out!" Really, I was afraid that he would leave me because I couldn't give him children. He would always reassure me that that would never happen, but my doubts would occasionally linger. I know Fred was trying to be strong for me, and I know he kept a lot bottled in. Society tells our men they should be strong and not show emotion; this way of thinking aligned with how Fred processed his grief. His fears were different from mine, and it was hard for me to understand.

Conflict and disagreements after the multiple miscarriages created a period where our relationship was strained. It took tolls on us at different times. We had to learn to fight together, centering miscarriage and its aftermath as a mutual opponent instead of squaring up against each other. We had to be comfortable being upset and angry but focus on not taking our rage out on each other. Fred and I never considered counseling or support groups. We never considered adoption. We desperately clung to our faith and tried to "keep hope alive," but the day-to-day nuances of life together after multiple miscarriages was constantly difficult.

We experienced a very sad time after each loss. I remember just lying in bed crying and praying. It takes time to feel like yourself again afterward. It's hard for those who have never experienced a miscarriage to console you or know how to begin a conversation. And you get tired of hearing, "It's going to be okay." No! It's not going to be okay. I'm hurting. I want to be a mom. Tell me it's okay to hurt. Tell me it's okay to be afraid. Not even those closest to me knew how deep the hurt went. We shared with close family and friends about our miscarriages after they happened, but never shared our struggles while trying to conceive.

I remember feeling very frustrated because I couldn't carry these babies and then I would hear these horror stories on TV and see others on the Internet about people mistreating their children. We would never mistreat our children. I know another couple who felt the same way. My friend and her husband had been trying, unsuccessfully, to conceive for years. I know they would be amazing parents. Sometimes the world just doesn't seem to make sense, and spiritually I struggled with this wicked reality.

In these moments of confusion and defeat, I turned to my aunt. Her and my uncle tried to conceive through the IVF process and had experienced multiple miscarriages along the way. She related to my experience and could offer something besides the standard go-to lines, "I'm sorry," and "Don't worry, it will happen for you." There were reminders everywhere I turned about miscarriage, babies and motherhood. My aunt understood that, and we shared in each other's pain.

At different times I remember telling myself that the pain was too much and that I wasn't going to do this anymore. But in my core, I knew that wasn't true. Fred and I always ended up back at, "Maybe one more time." Everywhere I looked there was something about a baby - commercials, billboards, magazines. Society puts so much pressure on women to become mothers and then saturates the media to feed into that expectation. Added onto this implicit societal pressure, is the explicit pressure of people constantly asking you about the timeline of that bun in the oven. Because people don't share their stories with everybody, and I didn't share mine, most folks knew nothing about the multiple buns that never made it out of the oven. But that didn't stop them from asking.

I wanted to answer them. I wanted them to know my daily worry that I might never be a mom; about how I walked around every day in fear when I was pregnant, never able to shake the thought that this baby would miscarry too. I wanted them to feel the tinges of jealousy I felt when I saw stories of married couples who conceived just three months after getting married and then carried the baby to term.

For someone like me who experienced loss multiple times, my world was different. I constantly walked around in fear. I feared answering people's questions, not wanting to jinx the pregnancy. I was anxious about walking into stores, knowing the baby products would be there waiting. I was too nervous to buy products, no matter how far along I was into the pregnancy. I lived in constant worry that I would never be a mom. Then we would get pregnant and the excitement would build again, and so would the fear. Every appointment was scary. Anxiety overwhelmed me and each time I would pray, "Lord, please let them show me a heartbeat." At no time did I lose that fear. We were always scared to tell people we were expecting.

All our miscarriages were in the first 12 weeks. We never got past twelve. We would hear people say, "You're not supposed to tell anyone until after 12 weeks." But our immediate family would always know. Then it seemed that just as soon as we had shared the good news, we would have to turn right around and share the bad.

With my fifth pregnancy, I was pregnant at the same time as my good friend. When she gave birth, she had a stillborn. She went through her entire pregnancy with no sign of anything being wrong, and then that happened. Fred and I shared in their heartbreak. Her loss also added to our fear and stayed with me the rest of that pregnancy. Even if we made it to 40 weeks, we could still go home without our son or daughter.

My fifth pregnancy was carried to term. The fear lingered on the entire pregnancy and even through the labor and delivery. I never felt assured that everything was okay until I heard that first cry from Makai. The relief that washed over my body with that cry was truly unexplainable. Our first child was born, and I finally felt fulfilled. Now I could say that I was a mom. *Thank you, God, for blessing me with a child.* I knew God had given me that gift and I was able to pour all my love into him.

Soon after, we welcomed a second son, JaSani, into our family. Then we waited five years and we tried again. We got pregnant and that pregnancy was absorbed by my body as well. Still no explanation as to why the body did that. That was miscarriage number five. We were able to conceive after that, but at 32 weeks my placenta stopped working and we had to do an emergency C-section. My third son Keoni was delivered, and we were elated to have another vibrant and healthy baby boy.

The pain lessened after having my boys, but I will never forget my babies. I still acknowledge each of my babies and I feel that one day I will meet them. I have tattoos in remembrance of them and everyday I'm filled with wonder about who my babies might have been. *Were you a girl? Were you a boy? Did you come through as one of my other children?* I'll always think about my babies. I have all my first sonogram pictures in a box and a journal that I write in when I think of them. On occasion, I may pull out the box and look at the sonogram picture and think I have a 13-year-old. Those five babies, they are still ours.

I think sometimes people can spend time attempting to compare losses. Someone might think, "You were at 12 weeks and that doesn't compare with someone who had a stillborn." A loss is a loss. Pain is pain. Grief is grief. Miscarriage and everything connected to it is a rollercoaster of emotions. There's really nothing anybody can say or do to make it better, but you just have to let the woman go through and feel affirmed in all the different stages. It's okay to be mad today. It's okay to be sad today. It's okay that you don't want to try again today. It's okay that you do want to try again today. A miscarriage is tough, and it sucks. It can consume you. It can terrify you. Whatever stage you are in, momma, I want you to know that I have been there, too and that there is another woman, probably somebody you know, in that stage as well right now that can help you get through.

3 JEN'S STORY

It was September 2011 when I married my sweetheart, Josh. While choosing to wait for marriage was hard, choosing each other was easy. He and I had saved ourselves for each other and planning our wedding and the night after brought much excitement. Until I started to do the math.

In April 2011, I noticed my period was starting the 24th or 25th every single month. For a woman whose cycles have always been sporadic, this struck me as odd. Worse yet, our wedding was planned for September 25th. The timing was horrible and being on my cycle that night was just not an option. I started doing research, and by research of course I mean frantically Googling, ways to adjust my cycle. I read multiple articles about how taking birth control would regulate my cycle. Though Josh and I wouldn't be sexually active until September, I started taking birth control just for that. I made a quick call to my obstetrician and began taking it months before the wedding. My cycle was regulated, and the plan worked - our wedding night was perfect!

A month after the wedding, I decided to stop taking birth control. I hadn't known that high blood pressure could be a side effect of taking birth control pills, but that's exactly what I experienced. The added hormones caused my blood pressure to spike out of control and I needed to stop taking birth control pills in order to lower the hypertension and prioritize my health. This meant that Josh and I weren't doing anything to prevent a pregnancy from happening.

In fact, our newlywed activity was just the thing that would cause a pregnancy to happen! While Josh and I were enjoying this newfound level of intimacy in the beginning of our marriage, our passion slowly began to fizzle when my husband lost his job. Those first months of marriage quickly became rocky as bouncing from temp agency to temp agency caused monetary stresses and marital strain. And it was in the midst of this unexpected financial blow, that a new development would occur.

Fast-forward to April 2012. I just kept thinking to myself *My boobs are really hurting!* Just to touch them was super painful and they were really sore. This had never happened before, so of course I went to research again, contacting my old friend, Google. I kept reading about breast tenderness during your period. Okay, I thought, but this is not just tender, this hurts *really* bad. Then I kept reading and saw that tender breasts were also a symptom of pregnancy. My mind raced as I started to go and look over all my previous dates on my period tracker. This could be happening. I should've been on my period, but it didn't come.

Then I mustered up the courage to buy a test. I peed on the stick and paced around. I went back to the bathroom and the test was positive. And then I broke down and cried for what felt like an hour. Where Josh and I were in our marriage wasn't the greatest space to bring a child into. Things between us weren't great, but they weren't at their worst either. While I support a woman's right to choose, for me, abortion wasn't an option. So I had to tell Josh.

I wasn't sure what his reaction would be, but when I told him, he was sooooo excited. I just kept saying, "I'm not sure this is good for us right now," but Josh remained optimistic. He couldn't contain his excitement, and he told people immediately. I quickly told him to "pump his brakes" and wait until after the first trimester, but the cat had already been let out of the bag.

I called the OB and went to go get the little bean checked out. The heart rate was great. When I saw the ultrasound, the tears started flowing. There really was something in there - and it was mine. *Holy crap!* I left there happy about being pregnant and wasn't as stressed anymore. I had never been pregnant before and it was finally starting to sink in that this was for real.

Though it was my first pregnancy, I think I felt what most women feel when they find out they're expecting - emotions that vacillate between fear and fantasy. *Oh my gosh, I can't do this! I don't know what to do with a baby. I don't like needles. How am I going to be ready? Will it be a boy? Will it be a girl? What name will we choose? Look at this cute outfit! I wonder when he/she will take the first step. Oh no, I can't afford a baby!* Every exciting and terrifying emotion that goes along with having a baby, I had it 1,000 times.

I was eight weeks pregnant at that first OB appointment and then I went again at 12 weeks. My baby was bouncing around like crazy. The nurses were like "Oh, this one's going to be a handful!" Although things on the home front hadn't improved any, Josh and I were consistent about our regular OB/GYN appointments. At our 16-week appointment everything remained normal and I was super stoked for the 20-week ultrasound appointment to be able to see whether I was having a boy or a girl.

I know there are blood tests nowadays to find out the sex of the baby sooner, but those tests also typically include the genetic testing that I didn't want done. I didn't see how the testing benefited me or my child. If the test came back with a less than favorable result, I knew I would be keeping the baby one way or the other. So I opted out of the blood test, genetic testing, and everything they lumped with it. I didn't want any added stress during the pregnancy. Doctors aren't God, and they don't know what's going to happen. I decided to wait until my 20th week appointment to find out the baby's sex.

It was July 12, 2012, the day of my 20-week appointment. I took off work that day. For whatever reason, the excitement I'd had for the appointment didn't surface. Instead, my anxiety levels were through the roof and I felt restless and overwhelmed. I couldn't breathe and I was nervous. I had a breakdown before the appointment. I couldn't figure out why I was so nervous. Josh said everything would be fine. Everything would be fine. Everything would be fine.

We got to the appointment and I sat and waited in the lobby, still uneasy, still uncomfortable. They finally called me in, and I thought to myself *Let's see if this little monster is a boy or a girl.* They put me on the table and put gel on the belly. And I didn't hear anything. Even when they didn't have the monitor set to heartbeat, I had usually still heard a faint woosh. Since I had been going to the same OB/GYN for regular appointments throughout this pregnancy, I had become familiar with the ultrasound process. I knew something was wrong because the nurse kept silently moving the probe around. I was thinking maybe she had the sound off. She was moving it around, moving it around. Then she stopped and asked when my last appointment was. "Sixteen weeks," I replied nervously. And she was like "Everything was okay?"

"Yes," I retorted, "Why what's wrong?!" Immediately, I broke down. Through sobs I faintly heard the nurse telling me she was having trouble finding the heartbeat. Everything in me just shattered. I already knew. I couldn't breathe. I was bawling. I could hear Josh saying, "The machine is broken. The machine is broken." I looked at him like *Shut up; it's not broken!* My anxiety level felt magnified by the news of this stillness, seeming to multiply tenfold as the seconds ticked away. I was shaking. I didn't know where my mind was at all. I couldn't focus on the realness of the situation. I couldn't focus on anything.

A doctor came in and they put the ultrasound back on. Then the doctor said, "I'm sorry to tell you this, but there's no heartbeat... But there's still a baby in there." I'm sure my reply shocked them, but I had come to this 20-week appointment for one reason. I asked, "Do you know if it's a boy or a girl?" The doctors didn't want to oblige. But I think the nurse took pity on me and she looked at the ultrasound again. I think it was then that she told me my baby was a boy.

I couldn't get out of the office fast enough. I rushed past all the new moms and visibly pregnant women waiting in the lobby. I just wanted to get home and actually cry the way I wanted to cry, without looking like a maniac in front of all these mommies. We went to pull out of the garage, but we had a flat tire. I was freaking out. I wanted to go home, and I was stuck in that place. I was carrying a dead being inside of me and that was driving me bananas. It was 45 minutes before we found somebody with a jack so we could get the spare tire on and I could get home to cry my ugly cry.

Later that day I got a phone call that I was going to have to go to the doctor's office and decide how I wanted to proceed. I could allow the miscarriage to go naturally. That would be extremely painful, I was told, since I was already so far into my pregnancy. They also didn't have a timeline for when it might happen. It could've been the next day or in a few weeks or in four more months. There was no way I could do that. I didn't want to do that. I couldn't just sit around and wait. The other options I was given were a C-section delivery, inducing a vaginal delivery, or a dilation and curettage (D&C). I didn't want a C-section. I didn't want that for the baby. I asked, "Can you induce me now?" The earliest availability was two days later, so I got mentally prepared to deliver my stillborn son on Saturday, July 14th.

We arrived at the hospital at 9:00 a.m. to put laminaria in my cervix. These were some kind of seaweed strips in my cervix that would pull the water from the amniotic sac to start the induction process. It was quite painful and caused cramping, and the doctor prescribed pain pills. I figured inducing would be a pretty quick process, but I was so wrong. Nothing was happening. So then they used Pitocin to induce me and by 1:00 p.m. I didn't feel any differently and nothing was progressing. So they added more Pitocin to get things moving.

Josh and my sisters and sisters-in-law were there. We were playing a card game to keep my mind off things. Usually I am the one trying to make light of the situation and staying positive, so playing cards with my family at that time definitely fit my personality. All of a sudden during the game, I felt a different kind of cramping. It was sharp and sudden, and I quickly became a ball of unbearable discomfort. I tried to stay focused on the game, but I could no longer make light of the situation. At that moment, I had to ask everyone to temporarily leave the room. I said something jokingly to the nurse before I got back in bed and at that point, I just lost it. The pain was telling me that stuff was getting real and I was about to deliver a baby that I wouldn't be taking home.

The pain continued to get worse. At one point I remember asking if somebody could lay on my stomach because it hurt so bad. I had to poop, but I couldn't poop. This went on for an hour or two. I asked the nurse if there was anything they could do. They gave me Vicodin since it couldn't damage the baby. I asked for another dose just a short five minutes later. I knew the nurse would say they had to wait to administer another dose, but I had to ask. I was in so much pain and nothing seemed to help.

At 11:15 p.m., 14 hours after being induced, I walked the few steps from the hospital bed into the bathroom. I tried to poop again, but still could not. The labor and delivery bathroom included a tub, so I took a bath to try to lessen the pain. I did everything they told me to do to soothe, but the pain persisted. When I came out of the bathroom, I had finally reached the point to where the baby was crowning.

This time the doctors asked everyone to leave the room. That made me wonder what else could possibly be wrong. A doctor came back with test results and asked if I was addicted to opioids. I looked at him like he had five heads. "No! I'm not a druggie," I retorted. Apparently, the doctors and nurses hadn't added the prescribed Vicodin to my chart. Only after it was confirmed that I was indeed not a drug addict, was it time to push. Doctors and nurses were in there telling me over and over again to push. So I pushed. Then I pushed as hard as I could and I just felt everything pour out of me, leaving only an empty womb behind. And once that was done, I cried.

The nurse asked if I wanted to see him and I said yes. Because there's no way I wouldn't want to see my baby. So I got to hold my little man. He was seven inches long and weighed 7.4 ounces. He had all his fingers and all his toes, and he had a little face. He looked like Josh, a very red Josh. He was red because his skin hadn't fully formed yet, but I could still tell he favored his daddy. I held him for a long time, probably upwards of three hours. The entire time I was hoping and praying for a miracle. In the longest 180 minutes of my life; I couldn't begin to count how many times I asked Jesus for a miracle.

I thought *Maybe if I rub his little chest something will happen.* I had heard stories like that about kittens and prayed it would work on my baby too. I knew it wasn't gonna work. But you do dumb things when you're stressed. Well, you do things that look dumb. Honestly, when it's a matter of life and death, you're not worried about how dumb you might look. Your only thought is that your irrational actions might combine with an unwavering belief in the impossible so that the outcome turns out in your favor.

The impossible didn't happen that night. With tears streaming down, I tried to hand our baby to Josh. He didn't want to hold him. I talked to Josh and talked to our son and then talked back to Josh. Then finally Josh held him. I know holding him made this nightmare real for him. Then Josh gave the baby to me and I held him one last time. I even took some pictures before they finally whisked him away.

Laying in the hospital that night with an empty womb and a broken heart was the worst night ever. All I wanted was to be held, but the tiny hospital mattress couldn't hold us. Josh and I clung to each other and tried to make it through the night on the twin-sized mattress. In addition to being physically uncomfortable and freshly on the other side of the most traumatic experience of my life, I heard babies crying all... night... long. So I ask myself *What kind of torturous human being thought it was a good idea to have people who miscarry on the same floor as people who are delivering babies and taking them home?*

My baby wouldn't be going home with me. In fact, they asked me if I would like to have my son cremated or buried with all the other stillborn babies. I envisioned a giant pit of dead babies buried together, like something from the Holocaust. No. No. No. I chose cremation and to this day I have my baby's ashes in a little silver heart. The heart was probably meant for beach sand or something else small and trivial, but instead it now carries something that means the world to me. I put it in a box with my pregnancy test, the clothes that he was wearing when I held him, the ultrasound pictures, and a few other items that I didn't have the heart to throw away. I would revisit the box once or twice a year or whenever I needed it.

With the death of my baby boy on replay in my mind, my despair and anger intensified on my walk out of the hospital. I saw pictures of babies on the wall. I saw moms with babies in car seats. I heard babies crying and saw the moms picking them up to soothe them. When we got home, I finally felt sheltered from the baby-filled world outside. To be perfectly honest, I don't remember what I did when I arrived home. I think for almost a month I didn't talk to anybody, not even Josh. I didn't talk to my mom or my sisters. I didn't even talk to my best friend for about two weeks. I just couldn't find the words. Friends were reaching out and texting, "Hey, how are you doing?" People sent food and flowers. I was numb to all of it.

I was numb to everything except Chico. Being in my bedroom with my dog Chico was my saving grace. He had always been my baby and now he knew I was hurting. He wouldn't leave my side. I read through the Hunger Games trilogy in two days. It was the one safe thing that I could read that would keep my mind off of the miscarriage; something that wasn't filled with mommies, babies or pregnancies. It provided a brief mental escape from my constant thoughts about losing my baby boy.

After two weeks of isolation, I started to realize that I was not okay. My thoughts became really dark and my heart refilled daily with a rage and sadness that I'd never experienced before. During those two weeks I got phone calls from nurses to check on me. I didn't say much to them but listened as they told me about a Rainbow group and a Heartstrings group. Finally, one day I thought, maybe I need to go there.

So I went to Heartstrings. They talked. I listened. A counselor approached me afterward as people were leaving and pulled me to the side. I felt comfortable talking to her one-on-one, and she gave me a number to dial. I called and was matched with a therapist. She was terrible. I'm a psychology major and I recognized the method she was using to just sit in silence until I broke. After three sessions, she still didn't change her technique, and I never shared anything. Seeing no benefit from the appointments, I eventually stopped going.

The only benefit I got from the Heartstrings group was learning about the Walk to Remember, a memorial walk for babies lost from miscarriages and stillbirths. I wanted Josh to go, but he didn't want to join me. Feeling hesitant, I walked alone down to this large open area and there was a pastor leading us to pray together. I got some rosemary and a flower and a little heart butterfly - cheesy things like that - to carry during the walk. I found comfort in being surrounded by fellow women and family members who had experienced a loss like mine. It was more helpful than I thought it would be. For the first time I felt some kind of closure. Nuggets of peace began to find a home amidst my buffet of despair.

By May 2013, Josh and I were in an even worse place in our marriage after having the miscarriage. We remembered the amazing times we had and agreed to stay together and work through this difficult patch. So I panicked when the oh-so-familiar tenderness of the breasts started coming back. I took a pregnancy test and I was pregnant. Instantly I was terrified because my last pregnancy didn't end well.

I called the doctors to say that I needed an appointment right away. They said that I had to wait until after I was eight weeks. I tried to advocate for myself, and told the nurse, "Listen, I've already had a miscarriage and I need this appointment as soon as possible." I was met with a matter of fact, "We can't get you in for another four weeks." I wasn't okay with that, but I said fine, whatever. I let out a groan of frustration and marked June 11th on my calendar.

On June 6th I had spotting and freaked out. I called the doctor's office and told them I wanted to come in. I asked Josh to come with me and he didn't come. I was nervous when they did the ultrasound. They said nothing was there, and I was in disbelief. I let them know about my positive pregnancy test and tell them that I hadn't gotten my period. They made me pee in a cup to test my hCG levels and they were really high. I was 13 weeks at the time they uttered these words, "We're very certain you started miscarrying." I couldn't even process what they were saying. There was nothing in my uterus at that time, yet here I was waiting to lose another baby.

I arrived home to an empty house and I laid in my bed and cried; and cried, and cried, and cried. I felt like it just wasn't in my cards to have a baby. I remember feeling very sad and having a lot of pain and a lot of bleeding. I went to the bathroom finally and I felt a huge clot pass. I saw this clot and I picked it up out of my toilet and I cried some more. I wanted to hold my baby again. Then I put it back in the toilet. I put it back in the toilet and I flushed my baby away.

I was still bleeding really heavily, but I left the bathroom anyway. I just went and laid in the room by myself and cried. The whole time this was happening, Josh was downstairs playing video games. And that was hard. That was super hard. But not as hard as my first miscarriage. I'm certain the second one was a little girl. The first baby was different. I had five months to talk to him, and I felt him when I rubbed my belly. With my girl, I only had eight weeks. I had no ultrasound pictures or chances to hear her heartbeat. The second pregnancy was less difficult emotionally because I had less time to get attached. Even still, I was real, real mad at God. I didn't understand why He would let this happen to me again.

July 14th and June 6th will always be days I will never forget. My due date for both of them would've been around the end of November. That Thanksgiving after my first miscarriage, I remember sitting at Josh's grandma's house and I knew that I would've had him that day. He would've been our Thanksgiving turkey. The thought of it had hit me like a ton of bricks, and I had to take a moment to collect myself.

After having two loved babies we couldn't bring home, the bond between Josh and I fizzled beyond repair. We reached a point where we decided that our marriage was done. In February 2014 we officially separated. I moved in with my mom and I started looking for a house. In May 2014 I bought my first home and moved in, just me and my puppy Chico. I resolved that my puppy was going to be my baby. Chico was my rollie for life. Dear God, make him live to be 120 because that dog is my best friend. I'm certain that the companionship Chico provided saved my life. There were many nights when I didn't want to wake up the next day. But God had a plan for me, one way or another.

I was content with my life and for a year I didn't think much about dating. Josh and I weren't together at all and didn't try to fix things after the February separation. There was zero communication. I wasn't legally divorced though, and that would become a messy three-year process. A year after our separation, I decided it was time to start dating. Who doesn't enjoy going out and racking up free dinners?! Since I had never really dated before, I aimed to make dating fun and carefree. I wasn't trying to meet somebody who would stick around; I wasn't trying to be locked down. So while I was "doing me," as fate would have it, I met someone.

I met this dude on a dating app and proceeded with great caution. Throughout my dating time I had met a lot of creepers and cray-cray people in the world. I learned not to give my phone number to anybody right away. You could earn my number after a week or two of chatting on the app. Well, this dude named Johnny wanted me to call him. He would write and say, "How are you doing beautiful?" That sweet talk didn't change my mind. He was like "Listen, I'm not a creeper." I'm thinking *That's what all the creeps say!* Then he tells me "Block your phone number. I just want to talk to you. You call me." So I blocked my number and gave him a call.

I second guessed myself the entire time on the way to our first date. I had my whole list of requirements; you know how we do ladies. He didn't have a car and I had to pick him up. First blow. Johnny wore orange camo shorts to the date. Second blow. He lied and told me he was 5'9 and he's like 5'7. Another nick off the list. We went to go get drinks and he was tipsy after three drinks. He can't handle his liquor. There goes another hit to the list. Despite a couple of first date blunders, there was something annoyingly attractive and interesting about Johnny. The next week Johnny wanted me to be his girlfriend, but I was still dating other people. Somehow, I caught myself falling harder and harder for this dude, until he became my only dude.

Then one day we started talking and Johnny asked, "How do you feel about having babies?" Silence followed. I didn't want to travel down that painful pregnancy road again. At my appointments after the miscarriages, the doctors made me feel like it was my fault that I lost the baby. I discovered the reason I had the first miscarriage was that my baby's placenta detached from the uterine wall prematurely. And I remember grocery shopping at Giant and having a moment where I doubled over in pain. Now I'm pretty sure that was when the ripping happened.

As a result, scar tissue was growing daily in the womb, and my son's nutrients were being steadily depleted. When the biopsy was done, a mass of scar tissue was found on the placenta. Somehow, they connected this to me being overweight. Though I know that overweight women can have complications, I also know that overweight women carry pregnancies to term and deliver healthy babies on a daily basis. At that point, I just didn't think one of those women could be me.

Things moved fast with Johnny and I, mostly because of our ages. With me being 31 and him being 10 years my senior, we both knew what we wanted in a partner. We met in August 2015 and he moved in five months later. Johnny already had three children, as well as grandkids, but he still kept bringing up having kids of our own. I wasn't taking birth control and we were sexually active, but we weren't consciously trying to conceive. Then in April 2017 I had a scare, but I was just late. The thought of a possible pregnancy stirred up a lot of anxiety. *I can't be pregnant. I can't lose another one.* To my surprise, when I got the test and saw the negative result, I started bawling. I was so confused. Why was I crying? Shouldn't I have felt relief? Then it hit me. I was actually sad that I wasn't pregnant. For the first time since I delivered a lifeless body into the world, I actually thought I might want to have a baby.

Everybody asks you all the time, "When are you gonna start trying again?" "Are you going to have another one?" You muster up all the courage in you to give a quick and polite answer while suppressing the anger you feel at the immediate opening of wounds that had never really healed. I talked to Johnny and said I wanted to start trying. I didn't want to mark my ovulation dates on a calendar or anything, but I wanted to start trying.

Three months later, I missed my period and my boobies were

sore. On July 13, 2017 I took a test and I was pregnant! I cried happy tears this time. I showed Johnny and he was happy. But the happiness didn't stick around for long; miscarriage memories soon clouded my excitement. One moment I would want to tell the whole world about the new bun in the oven, and then the next moment I would make Johnny promise to tell no one.

But the next day was July 14th, my official annual reminder that I had lost babies. Later that day, I decided to tell my mom and sisters about the pregnancy. This was a day that we collectively mourned every year, and I wanted this pregnancy announcement to add some joy and hope to the date. I told both of my sisters that I had a gift for them, and they needed to meet me at mom's place to get it. Because they knew what day it was, they honored my oddly impulsive request.

I Googled ways to announce a pregnancy and after browsing those suggestions, decided it would be easier to just give them a card. I found three blank thank you cards at home, and I wrote in them "Chico's going to be a big brother!" I gave one to each of them, and honestly it took everybody a little too long to figure it out. I was expecting an instant scream, but the delayed reaction still warmed my heart.

This pregnancy was high risk and not without drama. I went every two weeks to the OB/GYN. After 28 weeks, I went every week and saw maternal and fetal specialists for two to four appointments per week. I had a few scares during childbirth as well. I wanted to have my baby naturally, but he wasn't dropping and I wasn't dilating. Four hours passed and I was dilated just 1 cm. My baby's umbilical cord was wrapped around his ear. They put a monitor on his head to make sure his heart rate wouldn't drop too low. Then the doctors said, "We need to get him out now." I bawled when they told me I was having a C-section, but they took that little guy out and my life has forever changed. I carried him to term. I was in labor for 28 hours and I did it. I delivered him. I'm glad I tried again. If not, I would've missed out on the greatest blessing I've ever had.

While my sweet baby boy is the most amazing thing that's ever happened in my life, I don't want to try anymore. Somehow, I thought that once I had him it would help with the grief from my other losses. I was wrong. It didn't help. I still think to myself about the nine-year-old boy and eight-year-old girl who should be here. Even in the presence of my 18-month-old, the pain from other babies that I lost lives on. During anniversaries and the Walk to Remember, a scheduled grief washes over me like a flood. But even a song or photograph could trigger the waterworks any given day. I wonder what they would be like as their own little people today. What features would they have? What would their personalities be like? I know other parents who've lost babies are thinking this too.

4 ALEIX'S STORY

A tsunami. That's the image that comes to mind when I think about this journey of loss and miscarriage. Disruption and shaking at invisible depths to create powerful surges of movement above. Holding one's breath and pushing up against the surface with a desperate gasp of air only to sink back down again or get overtaken by an oncoming wave. Life-giving droplets seem to go against their nature, swelling to create walls of destruction and leaving devastation in the aftermath. Yes, miscarriage is definitely like a tsunami. Sometimes even as I gaze upon the blessing of my two amazing children, I find myself knocked back by an unpredictable kaleidoscope of feelings, vivid shards of memory from earlier loss and a nagging fear of more grief to come. I am regularly hit by tidal waves of emotion, but I am grateful that I am not navigating this unpredictable territory alone.

I am pretty analytical and a bit of a self-proclaimed data nerd. In my twenties, I was on a quest to better understand the dating process. I read somewhere that most people go on an average of 100 dates before they meet their partner. This was exactly the kind of concrete advice I was looking for, so I set a goal to go on 100 dates. For a whole summer I went on lots of dates, telling myself that the numbers would eventually work in my favor. What I eventually realized is that fulfilling a quantity quota is not hard. I could go on lots of dates. The quality of said dates ranged from edge-of-my-seat, begging-for-more interesting to watching-paint-dry, when-is-this-date-over boredom.

Ultimately this dating experience helped me learn a lot about myself in the process; my confidence and self-esteem grew along with my patience to truly wait for the right partner. Dating could yield a lot of interest but not necessarily the right partner. Finding the right partner would take time, commitment to my values, and a dash of divine intervention. It turned out that finding someone was not all that hard. But finding the one, a best friend to love forever, was much harder. I slowed down the roulette of dates and with each potential mate asked myself *Is this the kind of person I want to build a life with?*

James and I met on Match.com in 2012. Pretty quickly I knew he was the one I was going to marry. We dated for a year and a half and then became engaged and married. We talked about the importance of building a family and having children but didn't settle on a number. I don't even remember when we started trying, with intentionality or not, to build this family. I knew there were challenges to overcome and those challenges clouded my confidence. I had previous issues involving my uterus in my early 20s. First, I had endometriosis, and then what they thought was an ectopic pregnancy but turned out to be a low-grade uterine cancer. I was nervous from the very beginning that conceiving would be hard.

A couple weeks before our first anniversary we took an early celebratory trip with friends to Spain. On the trip I realized that I had all the early signs of pregnancy: breast sensitivity, frequent urination, et cetera. When we got home, I was excited to take a pregnancy test. I huddled in the bathroom watching the stick while James was building our new bed in the adjoining room. I came out of the bathroom, "Holy cow! We're pregnant!" I dodged the Allen wrenches, German-written directions, screws, boards and other furniture pieces that were strewn across the floor to make it to my husband's warm embrace. That was September.

By our anniversary the next month, we had lost the baby. That day I was leading a professional development workshop for teachers. The morning session had just come to a close when I was overcome with tremendous pain. I called my doctor and nurse practitioner and they both said, "Some cramping is normal in pregnancy." By mid-afternoon, the pain was so intense I knew that something was wrong. I left the training early and got in my car. Once in the car I was immediately regretting my outfit choice for the day. I don't like to wear underwear when I wear pants, but when you're having a miscarriage, underwear is something you definitely need. I stopped at a CVS a few miles from the hospital. Scurrying through the aisles, I did a double take when I spotted a pack of Depends. After a quick purchase and a change in the restroom, I caught a glimpse of my new look in the bathroom mirror. They were bulky and a poor fit with my dress pants. I waddled hastily through the aisles and made a beeline to my car. I felt humiliated, insulted, and alone.

James met me at the hospital and his presence offered immediate comfort. We watched the ultrasound while the technicians performed the procedure. A stoic, doleful silence flooded the room. The machine's *wom wom wom* sound filled the space. We knew it was bad, but they wouldn't tell us anything. We knew the absence of information was signaling the absence of a baby. Eventually, a doctor came in and shared the news and explained what would occur over the coming days. She tried to deliver the news of the miscarriage with a warm tone and supportive posture, but the added medical facts afterward made it sterile and impersonal. The doctor explained that miscarriage is common with one in four pregnancies ending in a miscarriage. Even with such tremendous probability, it felt terribly uncommon to me. And for the first time, data and statistics provided no comfort and no concrete path forward for me.

James and I left the hospital, fractions of the people who walked in hours earlier. At midnight we ended up at Walmart, ending our one-year anniversary at the checkout counter. With an open sour cream and onion dip container and fresh bag of chips, I stood there sobbing and eating, unable to process the unthinkable.

Over the next three months, the loss created some distance, but also a newfound closeness between me and James. Through fear and apprehension, we tried again. Many moments felt like we were simultaneously together and alone. James was supportive in words and actions, which made me feel connected to him. But at the same time, I knew he couldn't fully empathize with what I went through as a woman who was made to give birth to death, so I felt alone. Sex shifted from spontaneous fun to a more routinized quality. Ovulation was tracked carefully and when the most fertile day arrived, the so-called "green day", it was go-time! By February all our "green day work" had paid off and we were pregnant again.

But eight weeks later we would experience a second miscarriage.

I was out of town in Memphis, TN at an all-day workshop leading a school review with other principals and educators. I felt nauseous, achy, sweaty, and my calves were hurting. I didn't feel sharp pains like the first time around, but still I knew that something was wrong. The pains were becoming persistent and I called a friend who lived in the area to take me to a local hospital. Many of the details about the day are a blur, but I distinctly remember she arrived in yoga pants and a sweatshirt. I remember because she looked so comfortable, while I felt restricted in my stiff button-down blouse and tight work slacks. I had outfit envy, yearning for anything to make this ordeal a little more bearable.

Once at the hospital, the same heartbreaking silent tech appointment awaited. The doctor described the absence of a heartbeat and limited signs of fetal development. It felt like I had never been pregnant at all. Despite the pain, I was desperate to get to a place of comfort. I had my friend drive me straight from the hospital to the airport. I just wanted to be home. When I arrived, it was raining cats and dogs and our basement was flooding. It all seemed so awful and symbolic.

James had his attention turned toward the gushing water pooling in under the door of the utility closet. Rainwater seeped out under the cracks in the walls and inched its way across the floor to the legs of our couch and around the edges of the coffee table. I would not be able to curl up on the couch with my best friend. I was forced to sulk elsewhere, retreating to our bedroom alone while James scooped buckets of water to the outside of our house.

I had the miscarriage the next day on Wednesday. I went back to work on Thursday and I got on a train to Philadelphia for a regional conference on Friday. I kept busy. I didn't want to think about it.

I felt betrayed by my body. This was the body of a teacher who could teach from 8 a.m. to 4 p.m. with passion, only taking a bathroom break at the end of the day. This was the body of a principal who learned and performed dance routines in two days and then nailed it for the kids. This was the body of a triathlete, who could run, cycle and swim with the best of them. This was the body that had defeated endometriosis and low-grade uterine cancer. I could always count on my body to respond the way I needed, but not this new body. This new body kept failing.

Meditating on these failures became a constant and I got depressed; I kept losing things, not eating, not working out. I just didn't feel like myself.

Ten months passed before James and I tried to conceive again. This time I insisted on going to a specialist. The fertility clinic assured us that nothing was wrong. They had me come into their office and made sure to track everything: ovulation patterns, egg follicle size, basal body temperature and more. I felt so supported in the business of fertility. I loved the rigidity and predictability of the appointments. There was a data-driven process and a box to check off, and there was always someone ready to answer my questions. The clinic supported us while we tried again for a third time and committed to being by our side if something did go wrong. I felt there was someone there who truly understood. And for the remainder of this pregnancy venture, I would never feel alone.

I was out of town in Philadelphia doing some graduate courses for two weeks and on my last day in Philly I realized that I might be pregnant. My period was a week late and my body felt different. It felt like this time it was going to stick. I went to the bathroom of the hotel conference room and took a pregnancy test. I knew it! I knew it! It just felt right. I put the stick on top of the metal waste disposal container. I got home Sunday and took another test - positive again. I gave James the pregnancy test, overcome with a feeling of assuredness and confidence that wasn't there before.

I hated being pregnant, every minute of it. Well, every minute I was not at an ultrasound appointment. I had never had the opportunity to hear the baby's heartbeat before. That was magical. But outside of that, pregnancy was awful. I was sick all the time. I had really bad sciatica from between weeks eight and 30. I had to go to physical therapy two times a week. I couldn't get out of a chair independently. I had to cancel my trip to Croatia. In addition to the physical pains of pregnancy, I felt tremendous guilt that I was not enjoying this experience. I wanted so badly to be pregnant and yet couldn't find a lot of energy to appreciate it.

We found out we were having a girl and decided to name her Riley. Her due date came and went, so we scheduled a date to be induced. We started the induction process on Sunday and had made no progress after two procedures. The doctors asked if I wanted to jump ship and do a C-section. Nope, I wanted to keep going. I was in labor from Sunday afternoon to Wednesday evening, 63 hours in all. Ultimately, I had to have a C-section because Riley was stuck in my pelvic bone. All the pushing and inducing didn't work because she was wedged in.

The doctor described the C-section as unpacking your trunk and putting it all back in. The staff told me it would take no more than five minutes. I heard them playing music. They had tuned the radio to a smooth jazz and R&B station. First, I heard an Aaliyah tune, and then Maxwell's "Woman's Worth" was playing. One song played and then another, and then another. I quickly did the math; with each song lasting an average of three minutes and 30 seconds, I knew I'd been there for at least 10 minutes. That was twice as long as estimated. "What's going on?" I ask them and they say, "We can't get her!"

They needed two extra doctors. When they said wedged in, they really meant wedged in! But Riley did come out, and she was miraculous, and she was great. And everything changed after that. But the fear, anxiety and repercussions of loss didn't completely go away. I still feel like I am holding my breath; it catches in my throat. Sometimes the tsunami comes near the anniversaries of the miscarriages. On those days I think less about the babies who we lost and more about the grief surrounding the experience. I think about the loss differently after having Riley, and how the loss affects so many of my interactions with her. In stark contrast, memories of the loss also invite memories of birth. I then think about the super-human strength I had after I gave birth to my daughter. I felt like all the nerve endings were at the edge of my skin and I could do anything. I felt invincible.

I did feel invincible, until it was time to start planning for baby number two. The fear of enduring more miscarriages often outweighed the joy I felt as a new mother. I was in love with Riley and motherhood and ached to expand this love to another child. But I also felt happy with the joy from having Riley as our only child. Did we need to endure years of pain, disappointment and loss again? What would this do to my relationship with my daughter? My husband? Myself? When I thought about becoming pregnant again, I felt the collective pain from our losses all over again. I thought about the tremendous anxiety and fear of trying again.

The wave of emotions didn't subside after I had Riley, and the tsunami may not disappear for you either. It will come back in phases, and I can't say if or when it will go away. Hope, disappointment, fear, anguish and pain are emotions that resurge again and again and again. Even as I write this story, I reflect on how I navigated the storm and fought for air through every month of my fourth pregnancy. We have now welcomed a son to our family, Aaron, and as I watch him curl up and squirm into sleep, I take a moment to catch my breath. I can take in big, beautiful gulps of air in between the waves. The tsunami has still not subsided, but now there are longer periods of calm between the crests of the wave.

5 LUCY'S STORY

It was the year 2007 when I said the words "I do." Javier and I were excited to embark on this new adventure called marriage and anxious to start a family. When we married, we didn't know the many challenges ahead of us that would make realizing that dream next to impossible. I had a miscarriage in 2008 and then a second one in 2009. Each loss was difficult, and we didn't understand God's plan.

Javier and I didn't know how to process everything, but we tried to comfort each other and support each other the best we knew how. Through it all we only had one blowout fight. It came after the second miscarriage when I wanted to see him crying like me, and he wasn't. Together we made it through that storm and somehow kept our faith in God. We remained hopeful that our little niño would call us mami and papi one day.

When I became pregnant for the third time in 2011, my care team began to take more precautions. At 16 weeks I went into bedrest in the hospital, with the goal of staying there until I was 21 weeks. Though this would be just on the other side of halfway there in terms of our child's development, 21 weeks is the earliest mark of a successful preemie delivery. I just had to make it five weeks in the hospital. Just five.

During this time on bedrest my father visited daily. I had a wonderful support system made up of my father, husband, and countless family and friends. Despite the comfort from them and the care from my medical team, at 19 weeks I went into labor. Our baby didn't survive. We decided to have him cremated. If I had known the crematorium would call almost a full year afterward to tell me the ashes were ready and trigger the pain all over again, I might have declined the service altogether.

The grief was overwhelming. I didn't participate in any grief counseling and have never walked in the hospital's annual Remembrance Day. My support system and my faith were sufficient to carry me through. I had to watch cartoons and play gospel music constantly to avoid being bombarded by images of healthy, smiling babies. Javier did whatever I asked him to do to support me. We would go for walks in the sunlight to lift my spirits. He would run to the store to get whatever comfort food my heart thought might sop up my tears at that moment. In the middle of the night I would roll over and ask Javier to pray and he would always oblige.

Afterward I began to uncover a multitude of medical issues that made carrying to term difficult. First, I have adenomyosis. Adenomyosis is a condition that involves the movement of the endometrial tissue that lines the uterus into the muscles of the uterus. This makes the uterine walls grow thicker. It causes heavy menstrual bleeding and painful cycles. Second, I have three fibroids. The muscular fibroids crowd the room in the womb and make it difficult for a child to grow in the uterus. Third, I have an incompetent cervix.

Out of all three problems the last one is the one I knew the most about. With my third pregnancy my cervix was sewn shut from the outside, but the stitches became undone at the 19-week mark. I was thinking about trying again and the doctors suggested doing a bikini cut, opening me up just above my vagina and sewing my cervix together from the inside. These stitches would be more durable and create a stronger seal that would help the cervix stay closed during the next pregnancy. I had a day scheduled to go and have this procedure done but chickened out. I decided it was too painful to keep trying. I just couldn't bear the pain of another pregnancy that ended without us taking a baby home.

Protecting ourselves against another pregnancy presented another challenge. Initially I asked my husband about having a vasectomy. He was adamant that since the procedure was permanent, he didn't think that was the best choice. Javier wouldn't want to have the surgery done and then find out a year later that I changed my mind about having kids. He wanted me to have the option of changing my mind. So birth control became the answer. Each time I had brought the prescription to the pharmacy, there was a problem getting it accurately filled. I had to call my doctor's office back and forth three different times to get the specific prescription needed.

The birth control has paid off for almost a decade now. No pregnancies. No vasectomy. No hysterectomy. But every winter depression forms. The memories of my three babies come in like a flood. I have to go into distraction mode and pump up the volume on the gospel and change all the channels to cartoons. This past winter, I decided to take a vacation with Javier and it's the first time the weight of depression did not crush me. I think a new family tradition is in the works.

After 13 years of marriage you would think people would stop asking. But we still get asked all the time, "When are y'all gonna start your family?" My programmed response now is, "I have lots of nieces and nephews." I know that my siblings' children are not a substitute for children of my own, but the response lets people know very quickly that it's not a subject I want to talk about. My polite decline to baby shower invites does the same thing.

At the age of 43 I know that I have more time behind me than in front of me when it comes to starting a family. Tough decisions lie ahead about whether surgeries are needed to make my uterus a more suitable home for a baby, or whether it's altogether best for my health to have my entire uterus removed. What an impossible decision to ask any woman to make. While I have learned to be content with my life with my husband, I'm not yet prepared to say a final goodbye to the miracle of childbirth. Though the situation looks bleak, Javier and I remain open to the impossible becoming a possibility.

6 TAYLOR'S STORY

Thinking back on my story, my vocabulary seems inadequate to accurately describe my experience. What I went through was simultaneously less than a miscarriage and more than a miscarriage. I'm sure that comes off as an oxymoron, but hopefully at the end of this chapter it will make a little more sense.

With a background in public health as well as doula training under my belt, I approached pregnancy feeling very educated, competent and confident. So after a year of timed intercourse and tests that came back showing nothing was wrong, I wasn't surprised when IUI was my doctor's recommendation. IUI, or intrauterine insemination, is less invasive than IVF (in vitro fertilization, or the "test tube" baby). The goal of IUI is to use the results of multiple tests and data to get at least one good egg, sometimes more, to mature and exit the ovaries. Sperm is then injected up into the uterus as close to this egg as possible to increase the probability of a sperm fertilizing that egg. After a couple of months, we got the formula right for IUI and were elated to finally be pregnant.

From Week 7 to Week 11 of my first pregnancy I thought I might die. The morning sickness was unbearable. Even with the anti-nausea medicine I was taking, I was so nauseous that I couldn't eat. I was so nauseous that I could barely get out of bed. In addition to the nausea, I was constipated. The bathroom was becoming the place I frequented most, and I was in desperate need for a new hangout. I was a wreck, but that was okay because I was so happy to be pregnant.

Once the morning sickness passed, around Week 20, pregnancy was pretty easy. But that changed at Week 39 when I got a high blood pressure reading at my prenatal appointment and the lab results showed protein in my urine. I was diagnosed with preeclampsia (a pregnancy complication characterized by high blood pressure and damage to organ systems) and induced that night. By the next morning, still laboring, I was very sick. My blood pressure was high at 160/110 and there was blood in my urine. I was on magnesium sulfate to keep me from having a stroke because of my blood pressure.

Bed bound and sick as a dog, I gave up on my dream of a natural birth and that evening my daughter was born via cesarean. The hours after the surgery were not easy. I was on opioids to manage my pain, but they were making me hallucinate so I asked the nurses to stop giving them to me. I continued taking the magnesium for 24 hours, making me hyper-aware that I was still at risk of the preeclampsia possibly causing a stroke. I was afraid for my life. My midwife assured me I was in no danger of dying then, but in that moment it was hard to process anything she told me.

Bella gave us a bit of a scare too. Though she came out quickly, she was quite sluggish compared to other babies. APGAR is an acronym for the test used to assess the healthiness of newborns. Appearance, Pulse, Grimace, Activity and Respiration are all scored on a scale of 0 to 2, for a total possible score of 10 being the healthiest baby. The APGAR score is assessed one minute after being born and then again at five minutes. At the one-minute mark Bella's score was a 4. She had a gray color to her skin and was having some difficulty breathing. I think all the drugs I was on during labor were affecting her score, because she turned the corner right away. I was woozy from the meds and in kind of a fog so I couldn't see everything the nurses were doing. But after five minutes Bella's score had already risen to 8 and her gray color had faded before I held her for the first time.

At the same time Bella was fighting her way back to health, so was I. They don't tell you this about a C-section, but your abdomen fills with air. I had all this air in my belly and this next-level bloating was causing me intense pain. I was convinced that this pain from the extra air was really my liver deteriorating and I kept telling the nurses that I must be dying. Luckily for me, a nurse came in and drummed on my belly to let me hear the trapped air. Only then did I believe that I wasn't going to die, and my recovery improved steadily each day.

While in recovery the first thought I had *was I'm not going to have another baby. I'm not going to be able to have more kids. It was too dangerous! We both almost died.* The preeclampsia, and the complications that arose from it, simply seemed too much to bear again. My midwife assured me that I could have more babies if I wanted; I would just need to have them with the same guy. She said that the risk of preeclampsia increases with a new partner. She said nobody knows why, and that didn't surprise me. Preeclampsia is a "lady problem" and "lady problems" don't really get researched, unfortunately. Though she said I could have more children, I still wasn't so sure.

Three years later, we felt ready to expand our family; it was time for Bella to have a little brother or sister. While outwardly I was excited about having another child, inwardly I was fighting a battle with depression that cast a cloud over the joyous anticipation ahead. As a woman living with bipolar disorder, experiencing depression was nothing new for me. I was equipped with the tools, resources and support I needed during this low time in my life.

Although I felt "prepared" to battle the depression, I don't think I was quite in touch with just how depressed I was yet. I was very unhappy about my job, everything from the way my boss treated me to the devaluing of my skills to feeling disconnected from my co-workers. It all bothered me immensely. Though this cloud of disappointment and depression didn't seem like the ideal atmosphere to welcome a new child, that's exactly the headspace I was in when we tried conceiving again.

We decided we wanted to get pregnant again in the fall of 2019. I had to get a saline sonogram where they inject saline into your uterus and then do an ultrasound so they can look at the reproductive organs more closely. They wanted to make sure that the scar tissue from my C-section looked good. I was nervous about preeclampsia since I experienced it with my first pregnancy. So in addition to taking my prenatal vitamins I began taking baby aspirin, which reduces the risk or delays the onset of preeclampsia. Lab test after lab test was done to prepare for the IUI. I had done IUI to get pregnant with my first child, so I knew what to expect. But this time it was more complicated, and everything was harder.

On Day 3 of my menstrual cycle I went in for blood work and a trans-vaginal ultrasound (where the scope is inserted into the vagina) to get a look at my ovaries. On Days 5 to 7 I took Clomid, which stimulates the ovaries to produce more eggs. Eggs develop in follicles. When an egg is maturing, the follicles grow to a certain diameter; for an IUI, 20-22 mm is preferred. When the eggs reached maturity, I would then have to give myself the trigger shot, Ovidrel. The needle is inserted right in the stomach and the medication works to trigger ovulation. On Day 11 or 12 of my cycle, I returned to have all the labs repeated in order to monitor the progress in my ovaries and pinpoint the right time for the shot.

The first time I did this process (when I was pregnant with Bella), I went back on the 11th day, there were seven mature follicles, so they cancelled that cycle because it could've resulted in higher order multiples (three or more fetuses). This time, when I went back on Day 12, the Tuesday before Thanksgiving, and I had a couple of follicles that were in the 17-18mm range. They were maturing, but they weren't there yet. So I had to go back on Day 13 for more blood work and another trans-vaginal ultrasound. The first time, with Bella, it took three cycles to find the right formula, but then it worked. This time, I had to go back four times. Despite my familiarity with it, the IUI process overwhelmed me and the timeline seemed to be taking forever.

My declining satisfaction at work and the forthcoming pressure of the holidays likely made this IUI process feel increasingly extensive and draining. Though the Thanksgiving holiday provided a short reprieve from work, preparing the annual holiday feast meant that there was no rest for the weary. I was finally able to have the IUI the first week of December. Because Ovidrel is a similar hormone to pregnancy hormones, you're supposed to wait for the results of the blood work to avoid getting inaccurate results. Fourteen days after the IUI, I couldn't resist taking a home pregnancy test. It was negative. I told myself repeatedly that I had just taken the test too early, but deep down I wasn't feeling very optimistic.

The next day was December 18th and I went in to see if the results of my blood work would also show a negative outcome. They said my beta test (the amount of hCG hormone in the blood) was a very low positive. They usually want the number to be around 100 and my number was 10. If the number is below 5, you're not pregnant. If it's above 25, you are pregnant. All the numbers in between 6 and 24 are viewed as a gray area. So then I panicked. I was frantically Googling to see if you can have a beta of 10 and still have a viable pregnancy. And in true Google fashion, of course I find answers leaning each way. I saw women who have had betas below 10 with pictures of their beautiful babies in their arms, and then women who have had betas above 10 and lost their babies before term.

Two days later I had to repeat my hCG test, with the expectation that my number would double each day. It was December 20th and despite my loathing for my job and most of the employees there, I was capitalizing on free goodies and making small talk at my staff holiday party. I was not drinking because there was a chance that I was pregnant. It was difficult being fully present at the party because my mind was focused on whether or not I was pregnant. My thoughts were interrupted by a phone call and I snuck into a side stairwell to answer it. My doctor was on the other line. My beta was 19, which indicated a fetus was growing, but not quickly enough. "I have never seen numbers this low result in a positive outcome, but I never say never. So continue with the IUI process." Wouldn't you be ready to party after that phone call?

I made an exit for home to process everything and woke up the next day hesitantly determined to continue with the IUI process. That meant putting progesterone tablets up my vagina to thicken the uterine lining. I had to wear a panty liner during this time, and the whole process was pretty unpleasant. I had done it before with Bella and I had a successful pregnancy. But this time I wasn't sure if I would have a positive outcome. For two days I swear I felt "kinda" pregnant. I remember feeling my stomach churn at the thought of certain foods and getting hopeful. Maybe if I'm having food aversions, I am pregnant! At that point I felt slightly encouraged to keep doing the Prometrium (progesterone tablets) and repeat the labs in two days.

On December 22nd I was halfway across the country visiting my husband's family for Christmas. I went to the LabCorp to have my lab work repeated and they called me the next day with the results. The beta was 14. The numbers were going down. They told me, "You're going to have a period." I was confused. I had a positive pregnancy result. Was I having a period or was I having a miscarriage?

The term for what I was experiencing is a chemical pregnancy.

Because I had an hCG beta level that registered as pregnant (anything over 5), I was chemically pregnant. Only when the hCG beta levels reach 25 is the chemical pregnancy then seen as one that could be viable. But my levels never reached 25. So that's what I mean when I say it was less than a miscarriage and more than a miscarriage. I was chemically five weeks pregnant, so to many in the outside world I was "barely pregnant." But due to the IUI process, there was so much monitoring and blood work and labs before and during that five-week time period that the level of investment in and attachment to this second baby made the weight of the loss that much heavier.

We told our parents and siblings about the loss. A couple of close friends found out later. It was an unbelievably sad Christmas; one I will never forget. I started spotting the day after Christmas and I bled on the plane ride back the next day. Blood. Tears. Loss. Welcome home. The clinic said I could start the IUI process over again, but I never did. My husband was anxious to restart the process immediately, but I just couldn't do it. I couldn't do all that all over again and have it not work. I couldn't go through that again.

I had a manic episode after losing the baby and it created the perfect storm. The dark clouds of depression in the fall and the thundering loss of the baby that winter collided and the sky opened up. Everything came crashing down around me. I did some journaling and some prayer and some art to cope. But honestly, my first response to this downpour of hurt was nothing healthy. With me completely unaware, my miscarriage and the events following it led to a slow dissolution of my marriage. The loss of my baby and the loss of my husband seemed inextricably bound together.

Currently my life is so weird. I suppose during this global pandemic many folks are examining the changes in their life and adjusting to a new normal. Spending quality time with Bella during quarantine has certainly been an added blessing. I have a new job that I love and venture to each weekday through the masked streets and socially distanced crowds. But my husband and I are like ships passing on the night sea. We are cordial and collaborate to co-exist in the same house, but our relationship is a shadow of its former self.

Examining my life now, it's hard for me to think that I desperately wanted to be pregnant just six short months ago. I can't even imagine what my life would've been like being pregnant while parenting a toddler during COVID. Time changes perspective, and with new perspective comes new thoughts, new dreams, new emotions and new undertakings.

I say all that to let women know it's okay to change your mind about pregnancy and babies. Your post-miscarriage emotions may vacillate between sadness, anger, confusion, and maybe even relief. Wherever you are in your journey of pregnancy, infertility or miscarriage, however your feelings morph during this process, know that there are women everywhere sorting through this same mixed bag of emotions. And please be confident of this one thing - you can own whatever emotion you feel at the time. You are free to change your mind the next moment, switch your thoughts two seconds later, and no one has to validate those emotions - not even you.

7 JARONDA'S OTHER STORY

"If at first you don't succeed, try, try again." This Little Engine That Could way of thinking and persevering seems like an easy mantra to live by unless the thing you're not succeeding in is having children. I vacillated for months as to whether I would have my fibroids removed and whether we would try again. With every fiber of my being, I did *not* want to have that surgery. I had never had any type of surgery and the thought of the medical unknowns, especially as someone who has sickle cell anemia, was quite frightening. After chatting with Vince about my thoughts and fears, and after revisiting the possible surgery side effects and the doctor's recommendations, we decided we would try again. As I began processing what it meant to continue grieving while at the same time grasping the possibilities in trying again, I did what I usually do in huge conundrums - I turned to Jesus.

The spring and summer months had passed and my prayers for another pregnancy remained unanswered. A friend from church messaged me on the Bible app when she noticed that I was studying plans and highlighting scriptures about grief and miscarriage. She recommended that Vince and I try using ovulation sticks. She'd had a miscarriage early in her marriage as well and was now pregnant due to the help of the sticks she was recommending. I knew nothing about ovulation sticks at the time, but after reading over the link she sent I didn't see the harm in trying them out.

Within two months of using the ovulation sticks we were pregnant! I hadn't been to the doctor yet to confirm, but once my cycle was five days late, I pretty much knew a baby was brewing. I didn't tell anyone because I wanted the doctor to verify the pregnancy, and in some cases that made everyday living awkward. The prior miscarriage was in the back of my mind, and I wanted to be cautious and avoid doing anything that might cause harm to the baby. So when a group of teacher friends bought a drink for me after professional development, I felt stuck between a rock and a hard place. I took one sip, played the drink off as being "too strong," and then chased the sip down with a tall glass of water.

Though I didn't want any of my friends or coworkers to find out, I was eager to tell Vince the good news. The first time around, the doctor told us at the same time about the pregnancy, so I was excited about the chance to reveal it to my husband in my own way. We were planning a trip to Atlanta so that we could spend some time away together on the anniversary of Faith's death. We didn't know how it would be re-living that day together for the first time, so we thought it would help to at least have a change of scenery.

I ordered a special onesie and had planned to pack it and be ready to tell him on November 15th, bringing some joy to a forever-cloudy day. Vince spoiled the plans by asking questions about my cycle and why I wasn't wearing any pads yet. I ended up breaking out the package and telling him a day before we left for Atlanta instead. It's a moment I will definitely treasure. His smile lit up the bedroom. Joy emanated from him like rays of sunshine trying to touch down on earth. He immediately draped the onesie on his side of the headboard. That night, and every night afterward, Vince touched it and prayed for a healthy baby to be delivered.

The trip to Atlanta now seemed to be a celebration instead of an escape from reality. The hope of a rainbow baby had temporarily chased away the impending storm clouds of Faith's miscarriage. It was Vince's first time to the city of my alma mater, so I had lots of fun showing him my favorite Atlanta sights and eats. Then everything changed the third day of our vacation when I went to the bathroom and saw blood. Bright red blood when I wiped. Not a lot but seeing blood at all immediately took me to a state of panic. One thought raced through my mind the rest of the vacation. *Something's wrong... again.* I kept bleeding every day after that in varying amounts. A couple of friends had told me that their mothers bled through their pregnancies with them, so I was slightly encouraged that I too could be one of those mamas. But a few days after the Atlanta trip, I returned to work and I started to have doubts again.

I don't know what happened with the substitute while I was gone, but I returned to a feisty group of kiddos. My first day back, two boys were fighting and throwing things around the classroom, so I had to meet with their parents after school that day. I sat down in the chair to wait for the parents to arrive and it felt like I'd started my period. I stood up from the chair and turned to look down and sure enough there were spots of blood. I couldn't immediately go check on it because everyone else was outside at dismissal, but I had to stay in my classroom and supervise the two boys until their parents arrived. Twenty minutes later, after I'd spoken with the parents, I was finally able to head to the bathroom. As soon as I sat down, I heard a plop in the toilet. It was not a rush like during my first miscarriage and there was just one thing in the toilet. I have no clue what it was then or now, but my best guess is that I passed a small fibroid.

I scheduled an ultrasound appointment to make sure everything was still okay. Because of the number of fibroids in my uterus, my OB/GYN couldn't see anything with the ultrasound device in her office and I had to go to an ultrasound technician instead. On December 9th, the technician did the ultrasound and I was amazed by what I saw. There was a baby! I could clearly see a little human. And the baby was moving, doing flips and twists and turns. The technician kept calling the baby a little jumping bean. Then the rivers started flowing. Words can't really describe the relief that I felt when I saw the baby moving around on the screen. I hadn't seen that before and I was so overjoyed. I really wish Vince could've been there for that moment.

The elation was short-lived because then the nurse wanted to do a trans-vaginal ultrasound. Due to the bleeding I was having with the pregnancy that thought made me a little uncomfortable, but despite my gut telling me to do otherwise, I went through with it. I went to the bathroom to empty my bladder and came back into the room and laid on the table, anxious about what would happen next. As soon as I heard the words "Can you help me?" out of the technician's mouth, I had even further pause about what was going to happen. *Isn't it your job to perform trans-vaginal ultrasounds? If you need help finding your way around a vagina, then ma'am this isn't the job for you!*

As I was thinking *Don't let this lady in, JaRonda, something is definitely off*, the trans-vaginal ultrasound was underway. I could still see the baby on the other ultrasound screen, but things felt different. It hurt when she was moving the camera around. When she took the device out, the color of the blood was a more purple color that I hadn't seen before. I definitely remember thinking *Yo, I think she just messed something up.*

A few uneventful weeks passed and then it was time to get ready for the holidays. My family came down for Christmas because after our New York trip, Vince said that driving far during the first trimester was out of the question. On top of that, I wasn't really feeling very well. I was unusually lethargic and irritable and definitely not in the holiday spirit. I "faked it until I made it" during the celebrations. While I enjoyed spending the time with both sides of our family together, I just didn't feel well. I suspected another miscarriage might be coming, but I kept those thoughts to myself. I had been thinking that ever since the first sign of blood in Atlanta and the thought resurfaced during the trans-vaginal ultrasound. I asked the Lord to please not let anything happen on Vince's birthday or on Christmas. Not that I wanted a miscarriage to happen at all, but I really didn't want to have such a traumatic experience overshadowing those joyful days.

I needed to visit the doctor on December 30th to check in on the baby and run some blood tests. I received my hCG numbers back the following day, New Year's Eve, to learn that they had fallen by 20,000. I was home alone when I read the results because Vince was at work. I immediately went into a state of panic and was alone crying uncontrollably. I kept thinking to myself *This really sucks. This is not the way I want to start 2020.* Little did I know how jacked up 2020 would be... for everybody.

When I saw the numbers, I was speechless. I was feeling like something was wrong and now here were the numbers to confirm it. I was about to have another miscarriage. After the crying I got myself together enough to let Vince know about the test results. Then I texted my inner circle to let them know about the numbers and asked them to please pray for a miracle. They sent back encouraging texts like, "That's what the numbers say, but what does God say?"

We scheduled a second ultrasound after seeing that huge hCG drop. Vince made sure to adjust his work schedule so he could come this time. I could see the baby on the screen, but not as clearly as before. My precious jumping bean looked more like a cloud of black beans this go-around. The movement that was present at the first ultrasound was no longer there. Despite the stillness, the technician confirmed there was a heartbeat. The hCG numbers that came back from were lower than New Year's Eve numbers, but the drop was not as steep as the 20,000-mIU/mL decline. Vince and I cried and hugged each other, clinging onto this promising sign of hope.

On January 22nd I was trying to get to bed early because the next day was going to be a long day. I was scheduled to volunteer at this afterschool event the next day to celebrate the life of one of our former students who had passed away on that day a couple years ago. It was difficult to get to sleep and I woke up in pain around midnight. I took some Tylenol and turned on this "Baby Stay In" meditation that someone suggested. Putting on the meditation almost felt like I was a coach running a Hail Mary play. You know it's a long shot and the likelihood of touchdown success is slim, but it's all you've got left.

The baby did not stay in. Ninety minutes later, at 1:30 a.m., my water broke and woke me out of my sleep. I got up and went to the bathroom and sat on the toilet. Vince had woken up and was standing in the doorway of the restroom. I remember reaching down into the toilet and I could feel something long and hard and cylindrical coming out of my vagina. It made me think of the forming of the umbilical cord. When I felt that I knew we were losing another baby. I told Vince what was about to happen, and he just screamed "No! No! No!" while crying and pacing back and forth in front of the doorway.

Vince, who had now crumpled to the floor, continued to cry and scream with me as I felt my baby's lifeless body heading into the bowl below. It's a splash that I wish I could unhear. I was mortified that the best 15 weeks of my life now lay lifeless below me. This part was familiar to me because I was on a toilet the first time that I had a miscarriage. But everything that was happening was new to Vince and he didn't know how to react. He saw me in pain and at the same time he was trying to process losing another baby. Unsure of what was best to do next, he erred on the side of caution and called 911.

I asked him, "What are you doing? You called an ambulance?

Why did you call 911?" I'm sure Vince was right to make the right call to medical professionals who could check me out, but honestly when I heard the word "ambulance" the first thing I thought was, "Shoot, we gonna have to pay for that." I had never dialed 911 for an ambulance before and I thought that the response time should have been much quicker. It probably took about 20 minutes for the ambulance to arrive. Of course that 20 minutes felt like an hour. During that whole time, I just remained on the toilet crying while Vince kept pacing and checking on the ETA of the ambulance.

When the EMTs arrived and it was two males, I was already thinking about how the pair was not likely to be very sensitive to what was happening. While miscarriage affects both parties who created the baby, it is still seen largely as a woman's issue. The guys came into the apartment and I told them what happened. They asked if everything was still in the toilet and I said, "Yes, I think the baby is in the toilet." Then the two went to talk outside of the bathroom and I heard one of the men say, "I'm not looking through no toilet!" Then Vince went to talk to them, and I heard the EMT say, "Well get her together. Get her ready." Needless to say, that also didn't sit well with me. The EMTs left the apartment to go prepare a gurney for me and I began getting dressed to go to the hospital. I decided not to flush the toilet, nor did I look in the toilet at all before leaving.

Lying flat on the gurney, I felt every single bump that the ambulance went over. The EMTs were taking us to the closest hospital to our residence, but it wasn't a hospital that I had been to before. Arriving at the hospital, I was strangely greeted by a security officer that had a canine in tow. As a person with sickle cell anemia, I've been to several hospitals before and I've never seen a police dog present in any of them. Still lying on the gurney, I was rolled into the hospital. An ER nurse took my vitals and then I was wheeled out of that room and parked against the wall in the hallway. I'm not really sure what part of the hospital I was in, but it definitely wasn't a designated waiting room. The EMTs were also waiting around at the opposite end of the hallway, texting and calling folks on their cell phones. Again, that was my first time in an ambulance, so I didn't know the standard protocol, but I assumed the EMTs were supposed to stay with me until I was officially checked into an ER bed.

The hallway had different noises coming from everywhere: the beeping of machines, security on their walkie-talkies, and people talking to each other. I was trying to take it all in. The only word I have to describe my surroundings is dingy. I'd never wondered if a hospital was clean and sanitary until I entered that place. While I was lying on the gurney staring at the blinding white lights, I kept thinking how unsettled I felt and how I would rather have stayed home. My miscarriage would've likely continued to happen naturally as before, and there was probably not a reason for me to be in that filthy hospital with the extensive security and the disinterested EMTs.

I was so ready to go. Though my gut tugged at me to leave, my mind told me to follow the ER protocol and stay until I was examined and properly discharged. I don't know how long I stayed in the hallway, but I have a feeling it was easily over an hour before I interacted with anyone else from the hospital. Probably about halfway through this hour of waiting, I felt some very heavy bleeding coming out of me and onto the gurney. That exodus felt like the knife in the coffin, a confirmation for me that I really wasn't pregnant anymore. And there in that nasty, dingy hospital hallway I had my ugly cry; the kind of cry that doesn't care where you are or who is watching. It's a speechless declaration of pain that leaves you with nothing but a wet face, snotty nose and a headache.

Vince was searching for tissues or something to help me wipe my face. He found a pack of mini tissues somewhere and brought it over to me. We felt so invisible in that hallway. We were crying and mourning the death of our baby and people just kept walking by. No one talked to us. No one looked our way. No one brought us water or more tissues. No one came to check on my bleeding. No one asked us if we needed anything.

Finally, I got rolled into my ER room - well, section is a better word for it since there was just a thin curtain between the next patient and myself. The ER nurse came in to check my vital signs and asked me why I was there. Behind her I could see the EMTs completing some paperwork and it looked like they were ecstatic to jet out of there. I went through the short story of what happened with my ER doctor, letting her know that I'd had a miscarriage at home.

Then she brought in a third person for me to tell the story to, a student doctor who was shadowing her for the night. I don't remember his name, but that resident was actually the nicest person I met at that hospital. He had a great bedside manner and will make a phenomenal doctor one day. He started out by introducing himself and apologizing for the fact that the hospital protocol required me to tell him all the same information I had just given the nurse and the doctor. That simple statement meant the world to me.

The worst part of being seen in the hospital after a miscarriage is being forced to rehash the recent trauma multiple times. Each time I had to tell a different doctor or nurse that I had a miscarriage, and that this was my second pregnancy, and that I had zero children, it was like reliving my worst nightmare over and over again. Each reiteration of the story was filled with blades of truth that kept stabbing me in the heart. And I didn't want the story to be true. That resident understood that.

The doctor then came back in for some follow-up conversation. She suggested that Vince and I save the fetal tissue to be analyzed since this was our second miscarriage. The analysis would let the doctors know if there were any genetic abnormalities that could have caused the miscarriage. So at her recommendation, Vince took a rideshare back to our apartment to get a tissue sample, and to secure our ride home.

Somehow Vince mustered the strength to use a strainer to lift our baby out of the toilet and into a Tupperware dish. I'm sure during this time that my husband had his ugly cry. I can't think of how that must have felt for him to do that - to have to see everything and muddle through the bloody toilet water to find our deceased child. Now I think of that experience every time I use a handheld metal strainer. And I'm sure Vince does, too. That sucks.

Things weren't much better at the hospital. While Vince was gone, the Misadventures of the Gloomy Hospital continued. One of the other patients in the ER was screaming at the top of her lungs without warning every three to five minutes. Each time, two or three nurses would rush over to her and tell her that they were not hurting her, that she was okay and that she had to stay here in the hospital. It was almost constant for a solid half hour. I was just sitting there like *Lord, I hope she is okay... but I want to leave this hospital, now!* But the tests weren't back yet, and I hadn't had my ultrasound yet, so I had to stay.

A nurse shift change happened to interrupt my thoughts. On

the other side of the curtain I heard the nurse who was about to start the next shift talking to the nurse who just was on duty. To me it was just so unprofessional. The neighboring patients and I could hear all this "confidential" information. *Go have that debrief somewhere else where I can't hear you talking about me.* Then, as the cherry on top of this melting sundae, the new nurse came in and of course asked me again why I was there, even though I just heard the other nurse describe everything to her in detail. So frustrating!

I was still waiting for my ultrasound to confirm that all the fetal tissue was discarded from my womb. I was just lying there, bleeding away, waiting for my ultrasound turn and for my husband to return. Because I'd had a prior miscarriage, I now knew to tell Vince to bring me back a new pair of underwear, thick pads with wings, and some water to drink. I should have packed those things before getting in the ambulance, but it's hard to think of those minor details when you've just lost a baby.

The technician who would be performing my ultrasound came about 30 minutes later to transport me to the ultrasound room. I heard him through the curtain chatting with the receptionist about whether I could walk there or would need a wheelchair. The receptionist said, "Man, she just had a miscarriage. We need to get her a wheelchair." Again I thought about how the staff there really needed to work on their volume level, tact and overall discretion in the ER.

They found a wheelchair and the tech wheeled me over to the ultrasound room. I flattened myself on the table and cringed as the cold gel hit my stomach. Then the technician ran the probe over my abdomen and to my disbelief asked me, "Are you pregnant?" *Sir. SIR! Didn't you just hear that receptionist tell you that I had a miscarriage?!* In addition to that question I also had to answer, for the fifth time, the questions "How many pregnancies have you had?" and "Do you have any children?" I was fuming as silent tears hit the exam table paper, and I prayed to the Lord that the ultrasound would come to an expedient end.

After about 30 minutes the doctor came in and confirmed that the miscarriage was complete, and I would not need a D&C. These results were what I had been waiting to hear to know that I could leave the hospital. However, I still couldn't leave because Vince wasn't back yet. The ER nurses seemed unbothered that my ride home hadn't arrived. These people told me that if my husband wasn't back in the next 10 minutes that I would have to go to the waiting room because my stay was over and someone else needed my space. I couldn't believe it. My pants were blood-soaked. I was alone without a change of clothes. I had just suffered a physically and emotionally traumatic loss and they were kicking me out because my husband was 15 minutes away and not 10?

Luckily for them, my husband arrived before they instructed me to leave. The receptionist area probably would've turned into a yeller's paradise had they asked me to head to the waiting room. I waddled my way to the pay-to-park garage with Vince and vowed never to return to that hospital. Arriving home that morning was bittersweet. I was relieved to be free from that emergency room and its staff but saddened to once again be forced into living life after loss. The rest of that day was filled with sadness and crying, and I don't remember much else. We scheduled an emergency appointment with our doctor for the following day to take her the fetal tissue and to discuss next steps.

We were in the waiting room awhile since our doctor wedged us into her already-packed schedule for the day. Because it's an OB/GYN office, the waiting room was of course filled with pregnant women, babies and small children – a difficult sight to take in the day after a miscarriage. Finally, we were called back to the room. Navigating the hallway to the room was difficult because there was a nurse and a patient in the hallway chatting. They both appeared to be so infatuated with this beautiful newborn baby girl. The mom told the nurse she named her Kailani and the nurse became increasingly excited, as this was the name she suggested for the baby. "It means ocean!" the nurse exclaimed as she stared into Kailani's precious face.

Our hearts were crushed. Even though that whole experience in the hallway of the doctor's office was probably a total of 60 seconds, it stands out in our minds because of where we were in our grief at the time. She was holding a newborn baby in her arms and we were holding a baby that didn't get to be born in a Tupperware container. We left our baby there so the doctor could send the fetal tissue to a team of analysts. We also scheduled an appointment for a myomectomy consultation with a different doctor, hoping that removing the fibroids would stop us from ever having to experience the pain of miscarriage again.

The turnaround time for our grief was a lot shorter this time.

Neither Vince nor I missed as much work. The cards, flowers, meals and visits were less. We definitely still had our village in our corner, but everything felt different this time. It was almost as if we stuffed our grief in a garment bag and hung it in the back of the closet for a different season. If we didn't let our grief linger outwardly, we could subconsciously erase this horrible truth from existence and rewrite our story with a different sequel.

On the third or fourth day after going back to work, I woke up and I just couldn't do it. I woke up with tears in my eyes. I cried while I was getting dressed for work. As Vince and I were walking to our separate cars, I just started bawling. Vince heard me and came back to the car. He assured me that it was okay to cry. He told me that I didn't have to go to work; that I could stay home. I let him know that I didn't want to stay home because all I was going to do was sit around and be sad. I told him I was good; that after I got my cry out everything would be okay, and I would be ready for work.

But I wasn't okay and I wasn't ready. When I got to the parking lot of my school, I stayed in my parked car and continued to cry. I had been texting with Makeda and Ms. Richardson before work and we all texted that we just weren't feeling it today. Makeda walked by my car on the way into the school and saw me crying and hopped in the passenger seat. Then Ms. Richardson joined a few moments later in the backseat. They talked with me and listened to me and let me have my car cry. They prayed with me and encouraged me to continue to trust the Lord's plans, even when we can't understand them. Then, in true executive fashion, Ms. Richardson sent me home and asked Makeda to drive me. She said she would make sure our classes had work and coverage and would message everything to our administration.

When Makeda dropped me off, I was barely holding myself together. There was a cloud of sadness that hung over me the entire day. I don't know what it was that made that day extra sad, but it was. I couldn't shake it and I just had to sit with the sadness. Maybe it was because I went back to work too soon. Maybe it was something that I saw or heard. Maybe it was the replay in my head of me telling my first-grade class that Mrs. Dockett was not going to have a baby now. Maybe it was the words the pre-K sibling of one of my students said to me the day before that were echoing in my ears, "You lost the baby in your belly." Whatever it was, I let myself be sad that day, and was able to start again the next.

Then February 11th came, and Vince and I were headed to our appointment with the surgeon who would perform the myomectomy and remove the fibroids. While in the waiting room, I got a message through our healthcare platform with an update about the fetal tissue, the first update we had gotten in that three-week time period. The results from the tissue sample were in. The sentence that I read said, "Everything looked normal. This was a perfectly healthy male fetus." I showed Vince the phone and we both hung our heads. What an awful way to find out the sex of your baby! Definitely not the gender reveal we had planned. When we were pregnant the first time, Vince had jokingly said that if we had a son, we could name him JustIn Credible. Get it? Just Incredible! So we named our son Justin.

While trying to process the fact that we had a healthy son yet weren't able to carry him to term, we heard the nurse say, "Dockett" and had to shift our thoughts to be present at the appointment. What was difficult about attending a surgery consultation for fibroid removal after having had two miscarriages was that I had to sit with the fact that I didn't make this appointment after the first miscarriage. I even had family and friends imply that "Hey, if you would've had it done sooner then you wouldn't have lost two babies." I have to sit with that decision every day for the rest of my life. Of course people will say there is no blame, but that's easy to say when you weren't the one who had to make the decision. You weren't the one fishing your son out of the toilet with a strainer. And you weren't the one leaving the hospital without a child.

In thinking about everything we already knew about the fibroids, we pretty much knew we were going to have the surgery before we even went into the consultation. We wanted to plan the surgery for the beginning of June to make sure I had sufficient time for recovery and healing. I would take the last couple weeks of the school year off, and over the summer my family could come, and teacher friends would have more flexibility to visit and support me when needed. It was only February, though, and the surgery calendar didn't open up until the first of April. So I left the office hopeful, yet still nervous, with a calendar reminder to call and schedule my surgery in a couple months.

Three days later it was Valentine's Day. Vince and I aren't huge

V-Day fans, but we decided to celebrate this year and focus on us. We wanted to do something fun and spend some time away together. We did a staycation close to home to celebrate each other and get our minds off the miscarriage that just happened. We went to dinner at a restaurant in the hotel, saw a fabulous concert at a nearby casino, and got to enjoy each other intimately that night for the first time in months.

The next morning, I was putting on my bathing suit to go down to the pool, and I felt something down below. It felt like I was starting my cycle. I pulled down my bathing suit and got to the toilet just in time to feel a rush of blood come out. And this was not blood like on my cycle. *Was this the last part of the miscarriage that didn't come out before and got shaken up somehow during sex? Is this my first period post-miscarriage and so it looked different from my normal cycle? Am I hemorrhaging?* I didn't know what was going on! But I knew one thing for sure, I was pissed that this blood was messing up this pre-planned and pre-paid carefree weekend.

I spent the next hour on the phone with advice nurses trying to figure out if this was or was not an emergency. I didn't know if any more bleeding was coming, so I was fixed on the toilet for this whole conversation. Meanwhile, Vince had run next door to the CVS to buy me some pads since we didn't know how long the bleeding was gonna be around. It started out as a really fun Valentine's Day weekend but was ending in quite a different fashion. We concluded that it wasn't an emergency and tried to enjoy the last hours of the staycation. We lounged around and ordered some food for the remainder of that night.

Before we went home the next day, I suggested that we go to the movies. The sequel to a movie we'd been wanting to see was playing at a theater not too far from the hotel. We figured that not many people would be in the theater since the movie had been playing for a while, but boy were we wrong. The movie was packed, which to us was a sign that the movie was probably a good one since people were seeing it. We were so excited… until about three minutes into the movie. The last time we went to see a movie post-miscarriage, we chose an action-based movie because we thought it would be non-triggering, but there was a pregnancy and birth in the movie. The very first scene of this movie showed an expectant granddad rushing to see his child having a baby. Vince and I gave each other a look like that said, "You've got to be kidding me!"

Of course, that was not the focus of the movie and the scenes moved on from there, but it just seemed like the world was kicking us while we were down. And it seemed that would be the theme of 2020. One month later, a pandemic would hit, and I would be teaching from home virtually and Vince would be going to work every day with a mask on. A whole world of fear, sickness, and unknowns lay before us.

My surgery couldn't be scheduled in April for June. The hospital was doing essential, emergency surgeries only due to COVID-19. Of course, in my mind, this surgery is essential for me, but since it wasn't essential to me staying alive, it had to be postponed. On July 23rd, six months after Justin left this world, I was being wheeled back into surgery. My uterus was opened, and 25 fibroids were removed. Six fibroids were the size of navel oranges.

Now here I sit in my fourth week of surgery recovery, writing the final paragraph of my story. Though the surgery seems to have been successful and has cleared out space in the womb for a future baby Dockett, there are still months of uncertainty ahead. We know that our next steps are to get pregnant and prayerfully carry a baby to term this time. But we also know that we are not the one who orders our steps. I just feel immensely blessed to take each step through the unknown doors of conception, pregnancy, and birth with my husband. Vince remains a man who is caring, loving, prayerful and supportive. And still just as eager as I to feel that first kick.

Stay connected for more from the women behind

When the Heartbeat Stops...

JaRonda Dockett, Author

E-mail: whentheheartbeatstops@gmail.com

Social Media:
https://www.instagram.com/whentheheartbeatstops/

Social Media:
https://www.facebook.com/whentheheartbeatstops

Website: www.whentheheartbeatstops.com

Lynelle Herndon, Editor

E-mail: lynelleherndon@yahoo.com

Social Media:
https://www.facebook.com/LynelleHerndon

Jennifer Wang, Cover Artist

E-mail: Jennifer.a.wang@gmail.com

Social Media:
https://www.instagram.com/jenniferwangart/